C000018244

# OPEN LEARNING IN NURSING, HEALTH AND WELFARE EDUCATION

Kate Robinson and
Pam Shakespeare

OPEN UNIVERSITY PRESS
Buckingham · Philadelphia

Open University Press
Celtic Court
22 Ballmoor
Buckingham
MK18 1XW

and
1900 Frost Road, Suite 101
Bristol, PA19007, USA

First Published 1995

Copyright © Kate Robinson and Pam Shakespeare 1995

All rights reserved. Except for the quotation of short passages for the
purposes of criticism and review, no part of this publication may be
reproduced, stored in a retrieval system or transmitted, in any form or by any
means, electronic, mechanical, photocopying, recording or otherwise, without
the prior written permission of the publisher or a licence from the Copyright
Licensing Agency Limited. Details of such licences (for reprographic
reproduction) may be obtained from the Copyright Licensing Agency Ltd of
90 Tottenham Court Road, London, W1P 9HE.

A catalogue record of this book is available from the British Library

ISBN 0 335 19074 X (pb)      0 335 19075 8 (hb)

**Library of Congress Cataloging-in-Publication Data**
Robinson, Kate, 1948
  Open learning in nursing, health and welfare education / Kate
Robinson, Pam Shakespeare.
      p. cm.
  Includes bibliographical references and index.
  ISBN 0–335–19074–X (pb)      ISBN 0–335–19075–8 (hb)
  1. Paramedical education—Great Britain.   2. Distance education—
Great Britain.   3. Nursing—Study and teaching—Great Britain.
I. Shakespeare, Pam. 1948–  .  II. Title.
  [DNLM: 1. Health Occupations—education.   2. Education, Nursing,
Continuing.   3. Teaching—methods.   W 18 R6620   1995]
R847.7.G7R63   1995
610'.71'1—dc20
DNLM/DLC                                                        94–43323
For Library of Congress                                            CIP


Typeset by Graphicraft Typesetters Ltd, Hong Kong
Printed in Great Britain by Biddles Ltd, Guildford and King's Lynn

# Contents

# Acknowledgements

We should like to thank Mick Jones at the Open University for his contributions to the thinking of early drafts of this book and in particular for his work on Chapter 4. We should also like to thank Caroline Horwood for turning our 'small scale craft work' into an acceptable manuscript, and to the staff at the Open University Press for their patience as we passed the buck between the two of us as to why the book was not ready. The experiences and comments of a number of colleagues who are open learning tutors have acted as a real stimulus to some of our discussions. Particularly we should like to thank Marion Page, Jean Colbourn and Linda Thompson. Finally we should like to thank our friends and relatives who have had to spend some months stepping over drafts of chapters and been completely unable to see various dining-room tables for some time.

Since the majority of nurses and workers in the health care trades are women, we have used the term 'she' throughout when we refer to workers, students and teachers.

# Introduction

This book is very much a hands-on book. Although it presents some of the current debates that are important in the field of open learning in the health-care occupations, its main task is to address teachers who have to integrate open learning into their teaching roles. The book came to be written because of our belief that open learning is not a second best in the health-care context but an optimum learning pattern, particularly because of issues around the support of learners in practice placements. In addressing this issue we wanted to tackle some of the myths that seem to bedevil open learning to the detriment of its reputation in some quarters.

In writing the book we found that a number of preoccupations kept surfacing and think it is a good idea to spell these out right at the beginning. The first of these is that the teacher who is moving into open learning for the first time really knows what to do already; it is a matter of reconstituting the role that she already has. What is required is a reframing of the strengths of conventional teaching and a translation of the these into open learning programmes. Secondly the reconstituted role of the teacher will vary depending on the size of the open learning scheme in which she is involved. The larger the scheme the more likely she is to have a specialized role. At the same time we would suggest that the advent of such processes as desktop publishing means that there are opportunities for teachers to take on small-scale 'craft work' whereby they can tailor already existing open learning materials to the requirements of their own learners. Thirdly open learning materials involve some kind of paradox. Although they are sometimes called distance learning materials we have to ask the question 'distant from what?' For us the answer is merely distance from the teaching institution. Open learning materials can be much more accessible for the student than conventional teaching methods. Moreover, they can accompany the learner into practice settings making learning immediately available in relation to what is actually going on.

The reframing of the individual role of teacher obviously must take place within the context of the institution and that in its turn is contextualized by wider educational and health-care concerns. In Chapter 1 we begin by considering open learning in a UK wide context and looking at how it has come to be a significant part of the educational offerings of institutions who are involved in health-care education. We then go on in Chapter 2 to explore how a curriculum can be constructed in an open learning situation. Chapter 3 moves on to look at the individual role of the teacher and at how this is reconstituted in an open learning setting, using the concept of reflective practice as a way of examining some of the myths that exist in relation to open learning. Chapters 4 and 5 tackle choosing and adapting materials, with the assumption that for most teachers the generation of major open learning materials from scratch is not likely to be a central task. Chapter 6 takes a more pragmatic look at how the teacher's role will be enacted 'on the ground' and considers a number of settings in which a teacher can support the learner who is primarily using open learning materials.

*One* _____

# Open learning:
# towards integration

_____

Open learning will have a major role in nurse, midwife and health
visitor education in the future . . . open learning is no longer a fringe
phenomenon.

(Le Var 1992: 35)

The author of this assertion was then Assistant Chief Executive for the
English National Board (ENB), and she also cited support from the Chair
of the United Kingdom Central Council for Nursing, Midwifery and
Health Visiting (UKCC), Post-Registration Education and Practice (PREP)
project and from the Chief Nursing Officer for England. It is therefore
reasonable to suggest that open learning has, at least within nursing,
moved towards centre stage and away from being a topic of interest to
only a few enthusiasts. Major stakeholders within nursing education,
including the National Boards, the National Health Service Training
Division (NHSTD) and the employers, now consider that it is *the* teaching methodology that may deliver the solution to the problem of updating and upgrading a workforce of enormous proportions. While nursing
has been at the forefront of these developments, other health-care trades
have also followed this route, the Chartered Society of Physiotherapists
being particularly interested in its potential.

However, in order for the enthusiasm of the stakeholders for open
learning to be turned into open learning programmes capable of delivering high quality education to half a million health-care workers and
students, considerable changes in the structures and practice of health-
care education are proving necessary. Such changes cannot be imposed

on health-care education from without but must be generated and supported by the existing teachers, mentors and supervisors. Despite the fact that most were trained and developed their skills within what we must call, for want of a better label, conventional teaching, it is the central thesis of this book that they already possess almost all the requisite skills for open learning practice. What is required is a reorientation of these skills towards a new, but no less rewarding, role. Furthermore, we suggest, this reorientation, which is towards the facilitation of learning and away from the delivery of teaching, is already underway within health-care education and the introduction of open learning is therefore going with rather than against the grain of change. Nevertheless, it would be foolish to suggest that the delivery of high-quality open learning is a simple endeavour: it is a demanding methodology that can easily be misused and abused.

While we are not suggesting that such abuse is widespread in health-care education, there is understandable concern among many educators that tried and tested teaching methodologies are not abandoned hastily in favour of an untried innovation in which there clearly have been examples of bad practice. It is in order to demonstrate that good practice in open learning can be readily achieved that the following chapters explore the new role of the teacher in open learning and offer some practical advice on curriculum development, choosing and adapting materials and working directly with the learner. But first, this chapter will explore the concept of open learning.

### Defining open learning

There have been a myriad of attempts to define open learning (see for example Rowntree 1992a; Evans and Nation 1993; Hodgson 1993). Most beg as many questions as they answer. Definitions may involve phrases such as 'independent study', 'interactive learning', 'supplementary interaction between teachers and students' and 'flexible packages'. But then we are left with questions such as 'what is independent study?', 'what does interactive mean?' and so on.

The use of the title *Open University* by our major *distance* teaching institution has been the source of a great deal of semantic confusion between the two terms open learning and distance teaching (also known as distance learning). Distance teaching is a methodology that is primarily designed to enable effective teaching to take place even when the teacher and the learner are separated by distance. It involves the use of interactive learning materials as the primary source of teaching. They are interactive because embedded within them is a teaching and learning strategy that seeks to engage the student in the learning process. The devices that are used to achieve this, such as questioning, repetition, and self-assessment, will differ according to the type of learner, the level of study and the medium used, which may include video and audiotape and computer software as well as text.

To illustrate the distinctiveness of interactive learning materials, contrast an open learning text with a PhD thesis. The latter is designed specifically to demonstrate the worth of the author; it will be as erudite as possible – possibly arcane – and will develop the arguments as far as is reasonably possible, using as much supporting data as necessary to prove or support the argument. In contrast, open learning materials need not be particularly erudite and certainly should never be arcane. The argument will go as far as the targeted readership need it to go and the data may illustrate rather than prove a point. Things that would be deficits in a thesis, such as repetition, might be benefits in learning materials. We can therefore characterize the thesis as author-centred, the interactive learning materials as student-centred. The difference between the two types of text explains in part why many academics with substantial academic publication records nevertheless find learning materials difficult to create. The author must shift from a concentration on the needs of herself and her academic peers to those of the learner. The amount and type of attention paid to the students' needs will vary. Learning materials intended for those returning to study after an absence may have to attend very closely to helping the student structure their learning. Those designed for experienced students may assume a considerable level of competency in the student. The distinctive characteristics of the embedded learning process must therefore be understood by the teacher evaluating materials for use with a particular student group, and we look at this process in Chapter 4.

While interactive learning materials are central to the experience of the learner in an open learning programme, some aspects of the learning are usually dealt with through other means. Some of these might be familiar from conventional teaching, such as personal tutors, group tutorials, lectures, etc., although their place within an open learning programme may require some adjustment to the standard practice. Others, such as computer networking between learners and teachers, have been developed largely within open learning systems. Any particular open learning programme will put all these elements together in a unique package of elements, all designed to maximize the learning opportunities for the student. The Open University puts these elements together in particular ways and demonstrates considerable variety between the first-level courses, which have a high degree of tutorial and group activity, and the fourth-level courses, which have considerably less learner support built into the tutorial system and the learning materials. However, the various models adopted by the Open University are not the only possibilities, and subsequent developments have moved away from some elements of the OU models in two particular ways. First, as open learning has been developed for groups of learners who are not 'at a distance' and have considerable access to the teaching institution, the emphasis on linking the learner and teacher across distance has declined. Second, the possibilities within a distance teaching system for shifting control from the teacher to the learner have been increasingly exploited, and it is this development that has justified the development of the term open learning.

Distance teaching deals with the problem of the distance between teacher and learner by embedding the ephemeral and transient act of teaching into a set of materials. Clearly this offers the learner more control over the process. Whereas in a conventional system the teacher decides what and how much the learner will be exposed to in any particular session, within open learning the learner can make that choice. Nobody can stop her from carrying on to page 97, or skipping Chapter 4 or using the fast forward button on the video. The learning devices in the materials that were referred to above can be used to try and guide the rate and sequence of the learner's activity, but the degree to which they can do this is limited. Inevitably, using materials allows the learner control over the time, place and pace of her learning. This in itself can justify the use of the term 'open', but other proposals have been made that extend the range of the learner's control much further, into, for example, decision-making about what they want to learn, what medium they want to use for learning, the way in which the systems supporting learning are put together, and so on. Indeed, the Open University changed the face of British higher education (HE) by also offering learners control over *whether* they want to learn through offering open access. Most learning programmes do not offer this choice except to the most eligible learners because they define in particular ways those who are eligible to join. 'Openness', therefore, has a number of dimensions and can be sought in a number of ways. It is most useful to think of a continuum moving from 'closed', i.e. little learner control, to 'open', i.e. much more learner control, onto which any particular programme can be mapped. Offering learners control over their learning need not conceptually involve the use of interactive learning materials. But it is difficult to see how any but the most sophisticated learner could access and control the information and support she needs without some kind of supportive materials. Teachers do not usually work 24 hours a day and even when working may be needed by other learners and colleagues. The element of learner control so central to the concept of open learning is usually heavily dependent on the learner having direct access to and control over the learning materials.

Open learning therefore incorporates two separate concepts; the first relates to the way in which the separation of the teacher and learner in time and space is managed, the second, to the way in which power and control are distributed between teacher and learner. Evans and Nation neatly encapsulate the distinction while noting that it is not sustained in practice:

> Arguably, distance education is characterized by the use of educational technologies which assist teachers to span the distances between themselves and their students, and open learning is characterized by teachers' frames of mind, which lead them to teach courses in ways which reflect the needs, circumstances and interests of their students. In practice, the relationships between distance education and open education have been multiple and fundamental.
>
> (Evans and Nation 1993: 8)

In previous years, the first concept, that relating to distance, dominated planning for open learning, but more latterly, the concept of control has been the focus of attention (see, for example, Evans and Nation 1993). This development in part mirrors that within conventional teaching that is also trying to explore and expand the 'student-centred curriculum'.

Neither of these two elements in any programme – separation and openness – exists in absolute terms; considerable variation is possible and each course will be different. If we present each element as a continuum:

separation/distance _____ face to face
openness _____ closure

they can be used to generate a matrix that allows us to categorize learning programmes by two dimensions (see Fig. 1.1).

**Figure 1.1**

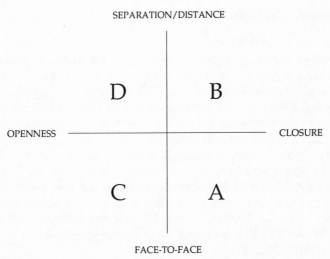

Using this matrix, we can suggest that a course could be:

A: teacher controlled and tutor/students are together
B: teacher controlled and tutor/students are apart
C: student controlled and tutor/students are together
D: student controlled and tutor/students are apart

For courses in which the student and tutor are apart but teacher control is maintained – through assessment schedules, for example – the term *distance teaching* may be more appropriate. Such a course would be located in quadrant B of our matrix. However, the more generic term *open learning* is increasingly used for all courses where tutor and student are separated by time and space and consequently parts of the tutor role are replaced by learning materials of some kind. While some of the learning materials may be highly structured and complex, others may be relatively slight, and again we will be discussing the various forms in some detail in later chapters. In this book we have used the generic term open learning, except when some specific point is being made and the term distance teaching is more appropriate.

One of the purposes of exploring the concept of open learning is that it can provide a map to those designing or introducing an open learning scheme. As with any change there may be resistance, and if allies are being sought then it makes more sense to look for them among those involved with the organization of courses located in adjacent quadrants rather than in the one directly opposite. And the way in which a scheme is 'sold' and its eventual success or failure may depend on the location of potential allies in adjacent quadrants.

## Open learning in higher education

As we have seen, it is impossible to discuss the concepts of open learning and distance teaching without reference to the Open University. The Open University, which was founded in 1969, was by no means the first open learning institution in the UK. It was predated by the National Extension College, and by the correspondence colleges, some of which date back to the last century. However, the Open University is undoubtedly the most important and influential open learning institution in the UK and possibly the world, and it stands as an exemplar of what we mean by a separatist institution, so it is worth dwelling on the history and nature of the OU UK. (Although the OU was the first institution of its kind, there are now a number of other such universities in other countries – hence the use here of the title OU UK; however, we will in future use the initials OU to refer to the OU UK and specify when we refer to any other institution.)

The OU was established as an entirely independent university. It has its own Charter and awards its own degrees. This degree of autonomy – a defining characteristic of UK universities – was an important factor in establishing the credibility and therefore the success of the OU, which at the time of its establishment was widely ridiculed within the university sector (Perry 1976). The characteristics of the OU include:

- it only offers taught courses by distance teaching;
- it produces and delivers its own course material;
- it directly employs all tutorial support staff;
- it registers its own students;
- it assesses its students and offers its own awards;
- its students (except for a small number of students reading for research degrees) are 'off-campus';
- it does not collaborate with any other institution in its principal activities.

There are probably a number of courses within the OU that do not fulfil these criteria, but it is an adequate generalization of the OU's work between its inauguration and the early 1990s. In summary, the OU teaches using the distance teaching mode, it produces its own teaching material, and it operates as a completely independent university. The OU is therefore a classic Distance Teaching University (DTU) – a category usefully developed by Rumble (1992).

The mode of operation, which can be categorized as *separatist*, was very important for creating the success of open learning. An alternative strategy of trying to incorporate the idea of distance teaching into a number of existing universities in the early 1970s would probably have led to the concept being entirely marginalized within the institutions. The OU depended for its success on the viability of the concept and operation of distance teaching and it has therefore acted magnificently as its champion. As well as the very tangible achievement of large numbers of graduates produced by the open learning route, the University has also generated much of the research and debate about open and distance learning. Obvious examples can be seen in contributions to the journal *Open Learning*.

However, the success of the OU as a separatist institution has not been without costs both to the institution and to the HE sector as a whole. Most importantly, the existence of the OU as a DTU did nothing by itself to alter other institutions of higher education. Whatever the needs that led to the necessity for the OU – Perry (1976) cites the inflexibility of access in existing Higher Education Institutions (HEIs), for example – they were not dealt with through the creation of a new institution, but merely circumvented. Existing universities were not challenged, but continued to offer courses within the conventional teaching mode and did not need to engage with the new teaching methodology of open learning. Few of the ideas of open learning were injected directly into the HE system by the OU although they have subsequently arrived by other routes. Indeed, one of the most remarkable aspects of open learning in the UK is the absence of OU tutors, many of whom are teachers within the Further Education (FE) and HE sectors, as a pressure group acting on their host institutions to change teaching methodologies (Perry 1976, asserts that about 60 per cent of the OU tutors were employed in further or higher education). This problem was predicted elsewhere. Rumble notes:

> Although consideration was given to the establishment of an Australian DTU, this option was rejected by the Karmel Committee, whose Report (1975) argued that such a centralized approach might actually inhibit existing institutions from adopting innovative practice.
>
> (Rumble 1992: 34)

Equally surprising at first sight is the lack of rapport between the OU and many of the newer universities – the former polytechnics – who were, under the aegis of the Council for National Academic Awards (CNAA), pursuing innovative and radical ideas about student access and teaching methodology throughout the 1970s and 1980s. This lack of partnership has proved to be a problem for both sides; on the one hand, many new universities are now struggling to acquire skills in open learning that the OU has in abundance; on the other hand, the OU is struggling to come to terms with the kinds of flexible entry and student-centred curriculum that are now commonplace in new universities.

A second 'cost' – or lost opportunity – is that within a separatist institution there is little incentive to construct learning materials in formats that would make them usable by other institutions. The institution sees its mission as teaching its own students and making its own awards. Again, the OU stands as an exemplar – materials are not packaged for external use and often come with a number of different 'bits', such as audio-visual notes, which are not available for sale. Materials are not broken down into the kind of small self-contained study units that can be easily assimilated into courses in other institutions; each curriculum is constructed and produced as a whole. An exception is obviously the development of the independent teaching pack – designed for external use either within practice situations or within other HEIs. But the production of such packs has until very recently been seen as a peripheral activity carried on outwith the central mission of the university. Interestingly, the independent learning packs have been largely produced by the School of Education and the School of Health and Social Welfare – both of which were centrally concerned with the education of an existing and definable group of practitioners.

Teachers in higher education have always seen the potential value of OU-generated and other learning materials but have largely used them as aids for themselves rather than sharing them directly with the students. Many teachers will be familiar with the strategy, when faced with developing teaching in a new area, of finding the relevant OU undergraduate text and using it as a basic framework for teaching. After all, if a team of academics have spent three of four years working on a set of materials, they are likely to include a relatively sophisticated review of the area! Nevertheless, the potential for taking this use further and offering the students direct access to the materials was seen by both the OU and others. For example, in the mid-1980s the CNAA funded a feasibility study examining the possibility of adapting OU material for use in polytechnics and colleges. The rationale for the project was:

> that there is a need for good quality open learning materials in the polytechnics; that good quality material exists in the Open University courses; that there is not an exact fit between the OU material and the polytechnic courses; that the material therefore needs to be adapted; but that the costs of adapting are much less than those of developing material from scratch.
>
> (CNAA 1987: 1)

More recently, the OU has begun to consider more seriously the potential of external sales of materials. A catalogue of selected undergraduate course materials is available and the university is willing to enter into discussions about selling whole courses with all the additions and amendments.

A third potential cost of separatism, which has been the focus of much recent discussion (see, for example, Rumble 1992, and subsequent correspondence) concerns the vulnerability of DTUs. They exist largely because they are different from campus-based universities. But if campus-based universities become more flexible and begin to service off-campus students, or if the concept 'off-campus' becomes less clear cut, then wherein lies the advantage of the DTU? Concern about its future as an entirely separatist institution may be one reason why the OU is increasingly interested in collaborating with other institutions.

Interestingly, the problem of separatism was avoided elsewhere. In Australia, for example, they decided against the creation of a large central DTU on the OU model. Instead a number of institutions were allowed to take on a role as producers of materials, and many other, otherwise conventional, institutions used these materials to offer tuition to off-campus students – they are known as mixed-mode or dual-mode institutions. The obvious success of the dual mode has led to all institutions being involved as they choose in materials production.

Within the UK, innovative schemes using learning materials in conventional institutions have taken a number of forms. The most concrete declaration of the dual-mode model within the UK can probably be found in the development of the Open Tech programme of the 1980s. This was a government-funded open learning programme that aimed to increase the access to training of the employed workforce or potential employees. The programme managers consciously decided not to fund a major central organization – in other words, no new OU equivalent – but preferred to award grants to existing institutions with an educational remit – mainly existing HEIs but also some commercial organizations. The hope was that the injection of cash focusing on the needs – both curriculum and logistical – of industry-based learners would re-focus the attention of the host institutions to groups of off-campus students who could not otherwise access education. Interestingly, a number of grants were made in relation to the needs of the NHS workforce, and the Open Tech initiative can be seen as laying the foundation of the expansion of open learning in the health-care trades. While the projects originally intended either to offer courses to off-campus students or to sell direct to individual students, it was realized by many early on that financial security lay in meeting the needs of large-scale institutional purchasers, many of which were conventional universities and colleges. The creation of the learning materials provided the opportunity for a whole range of schemes to grow up using them in different ways for different studentships (see, for example, Clark 1989; Green 1989; Johnston 1989; Wakeling 1989).

However, the Open Learning Foundation is probably the most interesting current exemplar of a strategy that develops the dual mode further into an integrationist mode. Formerly known as the Open Polytechnic, it was renamed the Open Learning Foundation with the demise of the term *polytechnic* in 1992. It is a loose federation of existing HEIs that pool funds and resources in order to produce learning materials that are then used for students in their own institutions. While this initiative has enjoyed only a modest success to date, it is based on the notion that open learning should be fully incorporated into the teaching portfolio of 'conventional' institutions. It goes beyond the dual mode concept of reaching groups of off-campus students and assumes that open learning can be helpful for on-campus students. However, it also recognizes the problem of the high cost attached to the production of quality learning materials and attempts to solve it by pooling resources. Health and social welfare is one of the areas of work that has been targeted by the Open Learning Foundation so it is of importance to our area of interest.

The enthusiasm of the Open Learning Foundation consortium members for the use of open learning within their institutions is based on a number of factors. First, it can be cost-effective; the cost–benefit equation is complicated and different for each occasion of use (see Robinson and Clark 1992), but the use of open learning may allow an institution to change the ratio of staff to students, and the consequent savings are likely in many cases to outweigh the costs of materials. A second consideration is the availability of staff to teach some areas of work. Even a major HEI with upwards of 1,000 academic staff will not have specialists in everything and cannot easily move teaching staff between specialist areas. However, in an era of competition for students, the availability of a broad 'menu' of courses dealing with many specialist subjects is seen as desirable. The importation of open learning materials enables a rapid expansion of the menu of available courses with none of the costs or problems attached to securing staff with specialist and possibly scarce skills. Third, it allows the institution to access students in work, either paid or unpaid, who find conventional timetabling difficult because of the constraints of work and domestic responsibilities.

In view of the resource effectiveness of open learning there is now considerable government support for the integration of open learning within all HEIs and a number of pilot projects have been funded under various initiatives. The emphasis, however, tends to be towards high-technology solutions to the teaching of large numbers of students rather than other forms of open learning including text-based materials.

## Education for health care

The use of open learning by teachers and practitioners within all the health-care trades – nursing, therapy and doctoring – has steadily increased over the last decade. We can trace that development through the organizations that have been involved and by looking at the growth and change in the range of open learning products available to the health-care education market. Much of the development has been opportunistic and relatively *ad hoc* – there has certainly not been a 'grand plan' or 'blueprint' underlying the developments nor have they been related to developments in higher education as a whole. They have come about as sensible responses to the kinds of problems that confront teachers in health-care disciplines. Some of these problems are those that confront all of HE, as discussed above. Others are particular issues within health care because of the nature of the work or the nature of the workforce.

One of the most striking features of the health-care workforce is its scattered nature; health care is largely delivered close to where the patients live and so the distribution of health-care workers largely follows that of the population as a whole. The closure of the large institutions treating patients with mental illness and learning difficulties and the redistribution of the patients into the community is scattering the workforce still further, and similar decentralizing developments are following in general health care. Besides the issue of geography, the workforce is also scattered in time because of the need to provide health care in shifts; the workforce of a single hospital or care setting will have a substantial variety of shift patterns and may never, in the general course of work, meet as a whole. Because of the geographical and temporal scattering of the workforce it is difficult to ensure that all workers have similar opportunities for updating and retraining. This is particularly unfortunate because of the need for health-care workers to receive consistent messages about practice standards and to maintain similar standards of care. The UK is considered to have a *national* health service, and there is a drive towards standardizing the type and quality of care.

These problems are largely attached to the employed workforce, but students experience similar problems. Health-care disciplines must be taught within health-care settings, and the students during placements are therefore similarly scattered for much of their time. Health-care settings are not conveniently grouped near educational campuses, and there is a perpetual problem of access either of the teachers to the students in practice or of student access to largely centralized educational facilities. This problem is being exacerbated as small NHS-based educational facilities are closed down and replaced by departments in universities that may be at some distance from the clinical areas used for teaching. It has been noted that while the use of open learning may decrease the physical connection between the student and the teacher, it may increase the connection between the learning process taking place in the classroom and that happening in the practice arena. Within conventional education a lecture or seminar has to be remembered by the learner in the practice setting, but learning materials can be actively used in practice. Moreover, they can be shared and explored directly with the practice teacher, just as they are with other teachers.

Open learning has been seen as a solution to the challenges of health-care education, and so considerable development has taken place over the previous decade. But the tension between separatism and integration, seen in HE, has also played a part in the current pattern of provision of open learning in health care. For example, the early development of open learning in nursing largely followed the separatist model. The Distance Learning Centre (DLC), which specializes in the production of learning materials and distance teaching courses for nurses and midwives, was established in 1983, funded initially through the Open Tech programme and largely followed a separatist or at best dual-mode model. Although it was established at the then South Bank Polytechnic – an institution with a large nurse-teaching programme – it was initially based in a different faculty from the nursing programme. The Continuing Nurse Education Programme, which was also funded by the Open Tech programme, was largely based in Barnet FE college – an institution with no record in nurse education but a substantial flexistudy programme. However, both initiatives also acknowledged that there was a highly developed national infrastructure for delivering nurse education and that the most productive policy was to concentrate on the production and sale of materials to conventional HEIs, and indeed also to learners working independently of any institution. This policy has since also been developed by the English National Board (ENB), which has produced a series of packs of learning materials designed to be used within educational institutions.

However, other organizations have retained elements of a separatist policy. The *Nursing Times* enrolled nurse conversion programme runs as an independent distance-teaching programme, although it has academic and professional accreditation and also affiliates with local providers who can become study centres. Similarly, the RCN registers its own students on its open learning programme run through its journal and organizes support centrally.

## Integration in the mixed-mode institution

The examples given above show that there is considerable variety among open learning programmes and that the links between producers of open-learning materials and courses and teachers in conventional institutions are increasing. Within these institutions the attractions of open learning are increasingly obvious for all courses, but particularly for those incorporating a practice element. The open learning roles available to the health-care teacher are therefore also increasing. She might be working as a part-time teacher for an open learning programme run by another institution, such as the OU or the DLC, and she therefore needs to understand the separatist open learning model. But she increasingly also needs to be able to develop her own open learning programmes based on the importation of learning materials developed elsewhere and operate them successfully within an institution that may be largely organized around the demands and constraints of conventional teaching. She may also have to deal with institutional pressure to produce learning materials for internal use *and* external sale, as the growth of open learning has been seen by some as a potential source of income. However, this last possibility is based on a misunderstanding of the complexity of interactive materials. Each OU course takes thousands of working hours to produce and involves a complex team of specialists including academic authors, academic editors, editors, illustrators, graphic artists, printers, and others – and some highly skilled administrators to hold the whole process together. Of course, the OU represents the 'Harrods' of open learning production and it can be done much more cheaply, particularly with the advent of desktop publishing systems. But nevertheless it is a highly specialist and complex endeavour and not to be embarked upon lightly

– particularly if excellent materials in the area of interest are readily available to be bought in. If the materials are not quite right then adaptation offers a cost-effective solution, and Chapter 5 looks more closely at the issues involved.

However, even within a mixed-mode institution, which incorporates both conventional and open learning methodologies into its core programme of work, there are a number of different ways in which the open learning could be developed. The institutional policy could dictate that it was fully integrated or kept separate at each of the three levels of the institution, the teacher and the learner.

### The institution

Some mixed-mode institutions have chosen to construct distinct units or departments with responsibility for open learning – this is essentially the DLC model described previously. However, this distinction can only be sustained by emphasizing the 'distance' element within open learning. Using Figure 1.1, it can be seen that part of the institution would then focus on activities in quadrants B and D, and part of it with quadrants A and C. Teachers who were most interested in the concept of openness, that is those operating within quadrants C and D, would be in separate parts of the organization and would have few opportunities to meet and develop their philosophy of teaching.

Other institutions have simply adopted open learning as a core teaching methodology to which all parts of the organization must subscribe. In this case all systems – quality, financial, management information, etc. – must be capable of meeting the needs of either a conventional or open learning course, and in general all staff need to understand the concept and practice of open learning. One of the authors works in such an institution that has the aim of delivering 20 per cent of its courses through open learning. Consequently, the needs of open learning are being integrated into all systems, for example, open learning is already integrated into much of the staff-selection process, the induction programme and the staff-development programme. Nevertheless, even within a truly mixed-mode institution a variety of approaches could be taken as to whether each teacher and student will be involved in both conventional and open learning.

### The teacher

A dual-mode institutional commitment brings open learning potentially within the role of every teacher. However, many such institutions have chosen to designate a teacher or team of teachers as the open learning specialists; in essence to divide expertise on the basis of the 'distance' element. The primary rationale for the separation of open learning teams from other teachers concerned with the provision of conventional face-to-face teaching lies primarily in the problems surrounding the production of materials – problems that are so considerable and that involve so much managerial input that it is easier to 'ring fence' them. However, if as we have suggested, open learning within a mixed-mode institution depends heavily on the importation of materials from specialist producers, the separatist pressures produced by the problems of production become less relevant.

There are a number of other arguments for segregation. It could be suggested that operating within an open learning delivery mode requires special skills – such as telephone tuition – so that only specially trained teachers can manage it. If this were so, there would be obvious pressure to ring fence and preserve such a scarce commodity. It could also be argued that open learning students require contact at times different from those required by conventional students – evenings and weekends, for example – and that this need cannot be accommodated within conventional teaching contracts. Finally, we can suggest that a teacher with mixed-mode responsibilities might bias resources towards the student she meets regularly and against the more distant, or less frequently met, student.

These arguments in favour of segregation of delivery rest on a number of assumptions. First, that the open learning teaching skills and the face-to-face teaching skills are so different that there is no synergy between them. However, the contrary argument is that if the requisite skills are similar or draw on the same competencies but used in different ways, then the general skill level would be raised if teachers were engaged in both modes of teaching. Second, they assume that open learning students are entirely different from other students and that their schedules and needs are incompatible with the needs of other types of students. While this may have been the case when the OU was founded and the vast majority of conventional students were immediately post-A level, the distinctions are much less clear cut today. Many students in conventional programmes are mature adults with domestic and social commitments. Some of them need part-time jobs in order to survive with or without a grant. The conventional 'working week' of study is not always convenient for many students and all courses, whether conventional or open learning, need to consider how the student can be best accommodated.

The idea that teachers will be unable to allocate their time sensibly in response to the different patterns of need generated by conventional and open learning students really relies on assumptions relevant only to the conflict between conventional teaching and materials development. In reality, teachers are familiar on a day-to-day basis with the difficulties of balancing the demands of different groups of students. New students are often insecure and fearful; experienced students often too confident for their own good! Each individual and each group is different and the skills of the teacher in part consist of an ability to adapt to these needs and differences. The differences between marking the assignment of a student you will meet in class three days a week and one who can ring you up at any time is not so great as to challenge any competent teacher.

For a mixed-mode institution, the overwhelming advantage of integration at staff level is flexibility. Staff can move between modes of delivery according to student enrolments – and this is a particular necessity within modular courses with a high degree of student choice. However, the advantages to the teaching staff are also very substantial. Each teacher has the opportunity to develop a full portfolio of skills – to operate in any of the quadrants of the matrix (Figure 1.1) depending on the needs of the learners and the curriculum and on personal preferences. For teachers who are committed to openness and who are reluctant to operate in quadrants A and B this represents a considerable expansion of opportunity.

### Learners

How would each individual student experience a mixed-mode institution? What, if any, are the advantages for them? The separatist OU is very popular with part-time mature students – but so are local universities and colleges and at the moment students largely opt for one or the other (although credit accumulation and transfer between them is available). With the choice of institution commonly goes no further choice of mode of teaching. But there are many reasons why a choice of teaching methodology within one institution might be attractive to students.

First, the expanded resources inherent in a mixed-mode institution incorporating learning materials are attractive to students who increasingly want to 'mix and match' within their programmes. Any single institution struggles to offer the complete subject range; the OU, for example, only moved into language teaching in the 1990s, and does not (at the time of writing) offer law. And although many of their management and health and welfare courses are of great value to health practitioners, specifically vocational qualifications are not widely available. This is partly because open learning production is essentially an industrial production method and relies on the cost-effectiveness of large numbers of students linked to major production processes. Courses will always, therefore, tend towards the most popular or the core subjects of the discipline. 'Brain, Biology and Behaviour' would be an example of the latter, 'Health and Disease' is an example of the former. There is relatively little room within such a system for a specialist course with limited student 'pulling power'. Neither can there be much room within a large-scale industrial production system for courses related to local issues and circumstances. Conversely, the local HEI has the capability of offering a more idiosyncratic course programme and changing it more quickly. Conventionally taught courses can be cost-effectively taught (with care) with a student population of less than twenty and put on (if necessary although not commonly) at two or three weeks' notice. And while the local HEI doubtless has excellent teachers, it cannot have national experts in more than a few subjects. In contrast, an OU course such as 'Health and Disease' attracts a range of national experts onto the course team or working as associate authors.

The Health Studies course profile at an integrated university offers an example of how an undergraduate degree programme can combine conventional and open learning to offer students the best of both worlds. The modular programme includes the OU's 'Health and Disease' learning materials as the basis for four open learning modules (although differently scheduled and assessed), and also includes a locally focused conventionally taught module – *The History of Health Care in Bedfordshire* – which is unlikely to be offered by the OU! Within this degree programme, and others within the mixed-mode HEI, many students move between open and conventional modes of teaching, either undertaking both at once in different modules being taught concurrently, or one after the other as they move between semesters. In the example of the Health Studies programme the first two of the open learning modules are compulsory so all students have to engage with the methodology. Thereafter, there is a mix of conventional and open learning modules on the menu. For each student, choice of topic combines with choice in methodology to offer a more complex menu to the student.

Within the field of study for vocational health-care, some courses in the same mixed mode university are offered completely in the open-learning mode. The question must arise of why a student would opt for the local university if they were going to study 'at a distance'. One answer may be that the particular course is not available from a DTU. Or if it is, it may not have vocationally recognized credits attached to it. That is not to say that DTUs cannot offer competence-based courses, and the OU offers teacher training 'at a distance', but it may be an area where the local university – local that is to the practice of health care – has a distinct advantage in achieving quality.

The individual student may have additional considerations. First, she may want to use other resources within the institution, such as the library or the sports facilities, to which her studentship gives her automatic access. Second, she may be offered additional contact with both teacher and fellow students because they are not at a distance. A materials-based course within a conventional HEI and targeting a local studentship can generally offer more face-to-face support and group work than a DTU. Third, she may want to move on to other courses offered in the conventional or open learning mode within the institution. It may be that open learning is particularly attractive to the student at this moment because of work or domestic constraints, but she knows that she will be able to access conventionally taught courses in the future. And while credit transfer between institutions may be available, registering at one institution and moving between modes of study is simpler.

The development of an ability to work within both the conventional and open learning mode is likely to be popular with students because it equips them with the skills for lifelong learning. There is increasing emphasis in higher education on transferable skills, and perhaps the most important of such skills is the ability to become an independent learner and to cope with a range of different teaching and learning methodologies. Employers in the health-care sector and elsewhere are enthusiastic about the potential for open learning and it is therefore important that all health-care workers understand the methodology, including its strengths and weaknesses. For this reason, among others, learning materials are also used within pre-qualification programmes. The pre-qualification nursing course within the integrated institution referred to above uses a range of OU and DLC generated course materials.

Chapter 2 looks more closely at the open learning curriculum, and deals with some of the key practical issues or challenges that have been highlighted by the discussion above.

*Two* _____

# Planning for quality: developing an open learning programme

_____

## Quality issues

We can easily agree that quality in open learning, as in any educational programme, is only consistently achieved by careful planning and management. In this chapter we outline a range of issues that will need to be considered in the course-planning process. But first, we will briefly focus on the questions: *what is quality?* and the necessary supplementary: *what is quality in the context of an open learning programme?* Within HE the concept of quality and how you define it is a highly contested area. The various models are usefully described in this excerpt from an OU document.

### *Five views of quality*

- *Product-based*
  Quality related to content of the product, i.e. the quality of ingredients (attributes possessed by the product). Related to inputs. Can be assessed objectively.

- *User-based*
  'Fitness for purpose', depends on assumptions about what users want.

- *Manufacturing-based*
  'Conformance to specification'. Excellence is meeting a specification precisely, and at the first attempt. Focus is cost-reduction by minimizing deviations from specification and by reducing rework.

- *Value-based*
  A composite of user-based and manufacturing-based. Quality as providing what the user wants at an acceptable price, and conformance to specification at an acceptable cost. Quality (a measure of excellence) is equated with value (a measure of worth).

- *Transcendent*
  Quality as innate excellence. Cannot be precisely defined or measured, recognizable only through experience (e.g. appreciation of a painting).
  ('Project Management', OU 1987, cited in Robinson 1992)

It is likely that all these views of quality come into play in different parts of the educational process, although the current emphasis is on the notion of 'fitness for purpose' with its focus on the importance of the customers' perspectives. However, because an open learning course contains a tangible and substantial input in the form of a set of learning materials, there is a considerable danger that attention will focus on that to the exclusion of other aspects of the programme. This focus on courseware has its most obvious manifestation in the desire for a 'guaranteed' product, and the idea of a 'kitemark' for courseware has been around within open learning for some time. In nursing, for example, there have been suggestions that the ENB 'kitemark' a range of producers' courseware in order that teachers, many of them new to open learning, could more easily choose 'good', i.e. kitemarked, materials. Discussions have also taken place within the European Union on the kitemarking of open learning materials (Robinson 1992).

It is easy to see the attraction of this idea, and kitemarking might usefully eliminate some of the worst courseware from the market. However, it assumes that the question 'Which learning materials are good?' is sufficient, but any educational programme involves more than just the learning materials. It involves the recruitment process, the face-to-face work, the assessment, and for many clinical courses, the focused clinical experience. Any curriculum must focus on all these, and an open learning curriculum is no less complex than a conventional one. Indeed, in some ways it is more complex, as the addition of a new component – the set of learning materials – means that a new range of relationships will need to be established with each of the other components in the educational process. Robinson (1992: 12) suggests that 'Distance and open learning usually has more complex systems and involves more roles and players in its enactment, particularly when large scale. Therefore attempts to locate and manage quality in open and distance learning need to take account of the multiple perspectives involved and the often complex and interlocking systems. The adoption of open learning as the mode of delivery therefore requires considerable detailed forward planning to ensure that all the parts fit together, and a holistic overview to ensure that the students experience the course as a seamless whole. A useful approach is therefore to take a holistic curriculum-based approach to achieving quality. Each aspect of the curriculum should be examined to see how openness is generated and whether it is well managed. The learning materials and the 'face work' must be organized to complement each other rather than conflict.

A major early task for the course development team is the placement of the curriculum roughly among the possibilities suggested by Figure 1.1. Is the main emphasis to be on the distance aspects or the openness aspects or both? Is this to be an integrated course, aiming to reap the benefits of both open and conventional learning systems, or is it more important to make it available to off-campus students? The central concern should be fitness for purpose, and the issues could include the need:

- to increase access to the programme for practitioners who would, because of the demands of practice, be unable to attend regularly and frequently;
- to increase access for people with social and domestic responsibilities who cannot attend regularly and frequently;
- to reduce the pressure on the teaching accommodation;
- to include on the menu of subjects one which the institution would not otherwise have the resources to offer;
- to allow students access to national and international experts who could not otherwise be available to teach the course;
- to reduce the direct costs to the customers;
- to increase the profit to be generated;
- to encourage the students to develop skills in independent learning;
- to encourage the students to form self-help groups and learn to support their colleagues' learning;
- to ensure that the learning offered to a large group of people is consistent.

Any particular course will put these aims together in specific combinations. For example, for open learning courses aiming to develop second-level nurses into first-level nurses the choice of the open learning mode may be because the cost of conventional full-time courses restricts access especially to the many second-level nurses who are women working part-time with substantial domestic commitments. A course on Information Technology (IT) may need to be offered to every practitioner in an organization regardless of shift and therefore, while ease of access is important, it is also essential that the information about the IT system is given consistently and accurately and therefore an ephemeral presentation that may change over time is not appropriate.

### The process of curriculum development in open learning

Once the reasons for choosing open learning are clearly established, they should inform the decision-making throughout the curriculum-development process. For example, if an aim is to increase access and the numbers on the course, then the discussion on practice placements would have to consider increasing the number of placement opportunities. However, improving access may be designed to equalize opportunity rather than increase numbers, so attention would therefore be directed to different areas. A course aiming to increase access by those with domestic responsibilities could not be compatible with a library that closes at 5 pm. Similarly, the course evaluation process must be able to provide data to inform a discussion about whether the particular chosen aims have been met.

A curriculum is basically a map of the planned student learning experience. It begins with a discussion of the overall aims of the course; for example, a course might aim to prepare a student for initial registration as a practitioner or to develop a reflective practitioner. It might be concerned with developing a particular skill or competence or with changing the students' value systems. Once the aim is established there is further development of the nature of the necessary inputs – teachers, classrooms, learning resources, etc. – and processes – lessons, assignments, etc. Normally an evaluation programme would also be required. All of these inputs and processes are located with reference to some specified group of students fixed in time and space and to an organizational context.

Commonly, a curriculum will be developed and approved without any great degree of specification of process. For example, a 'lecture' and paired 'tutorial' could be scheduled to explore the health-care needs of elderly people. The teachers will subsequently use that as the basis for a more detailed specification and the teaching activity will take place at the allotted time and in the allocated space. The act of bringing the curriculum to life in any particular instance is a developmental one; each 'lesson' is an adventure for teacher and learners and the experience of each lesson is used by the teacher to improve the session when it is done again. This will differ fundamentally in an open learning programme context; even the first step – the exposition of the course aims will need some amendment – but thereafter the whole process begins to differ more radically.

### *The process of curriculum development*

In an open learning programme a very substantial part of the teaching process – commonly up to 90 per cent – will be embedded in a set of learning materials. The generation of learning materials, like the production of a lesson, is a complex, developmental process. But, unlike the face-to-face teaching process, it must be completed before it can be shared with learners. This does not indicate that an open learning course is static and cannot evolve. All the processes other than the materials production are as ephemeral as in any conventionally taught course, and even the materials can be amended. However, the presence of the learning materials must be acknowledged in the process of curriculum development. There are perhaps two contrasting models of open learning curriculum development – probably neither ever seen in its pure form and they are probably best conceptualized as different ends of a spectrum. We will characterize these crudely as curriculum-led and materials-led.

*Curriculum-led open learning*
In this model a curriculum is developed as usual, without any reference to the learning materials. Specifications are written, teaching styles and content defined. Once all aspects of the curriculum are agreed, and sometimes after the curriculum has been presented in the conventional mode, there will be an attempt to find existing open learning materials that fit into the specification. This approach is sometimes used because an institution wants to increase its use of open learning within a portfolio of existing courses, because of a change in the studentship for example. However, the process is difficult to complete successfully for a number of reasons. Primarily, if no prior thought has been given to the logistical and philosophical 'shape' of the available learning materials then it is unlikely that any will be found to fit. It is as if a jigsaw has been constructed with one piece missing – the likelihood of just that shape and picture having been developed elsewhere is remote. Nevertheless, it does sometimes work out, especially if the course team is prepared to use the opportunity of change to review a number of other aspects of the curriculum and to adapt the learning materials along the lines suggested in Chapter 5.

*Materials-led open learning*
In the alternative model the learning materials form the foundation for everything else. A set of materials is chosen and a curriculum is developed around it with every aspect directed by the shape of the materials. This mode of curriculum development is perhaps most appropriate for an open learning or resource centre that offers programmes to a wide variety of students and can work by developing a course and then looking around for a studentship. However, teachers within health care are working with a very specific studentship and with specific goals in mind. A superb set of materials on, say, the History of Art may be enticing but is difficult to justify its use to either the accrediting bodies or the purchasers of education!

If neither of these models is wholly appropriate – the first because it rarely works, and the second because it is insufficiently sensitive to organizational goals, then what approach will work? An alternative methodology combines aspects of both the curriculum-led model and the materials-led model and can be characterized as *iterative*.

### The iterative model

As the name suggests, this involves a continuous dialogue between the curriculum and one or more sets of learning materials. The process starts with the development of an outline curriculum. The essential components are a description of the intended studentship and a broad outline of the aims of the programme, including the needs of any external accrediting agency; an outline educational philosophy is also important. A very rough trawl of likely or possible materials can then take place. At this stage it is not necessary to be too concerned about matching the academic level or the content details of the materials to the outline specification, but you may wish to define, even at this stage, some absolute constraints. For example, materials that do not acknowledge the diversity of people may not be acceptable and should therefore be discarded immediately. Positive aspects of the menu of possible or potential learning materials can be fed into the developing curriculum; issues that the team has not previously considered may now emerge as important. The materials can be used as a vehicle to enable the team to clarify and revise their plans. A workshop for the course-development team with a whole range of materials to explore and discuss can be very productive. As 'good' and 'bad' examples are found the team can generate very clear ideas about the sort of substantive content and value system that they want the students to experience. As this process continues the curriculum will be developed, detail can be written in, and simultaneously potential learning materials will be eliminated until only one choice remains. This is not just the 'best fit', as in the curriculum-led model above, because the materials have been used to build the curriculum. But neither has the curriculum taken second place, as in the materials-led model, because the curriculum has taken ideas from a number of other sources. Because of this, the package of materials may not 'fit' exactly into the curriculum, but it will be compatible with most aspects of it. It may appear that the discrepancies are large, for example, the courseware may be designed for a different academic level or it may omit a substantial section of the aims, but there are many ways of compensating for this through other aspects of the course. The materials may be adapted or enhanced, and we deal with these issues in Chapter 5.

Having discussed the *process* of developing the curriculum, the following sections look in more detail at different aspects in order to highlight open learning issues.

**Maximizing the value of the materials**

While the materials are not necessarily the most important part of the curriculum, they need to be considered carefully because they may generate particular models for the ways in which other aspects of the programme should be organized or impose constraints on what can sensibly be done. Three particular issues need consideration:

- pacing;
- resourcing;
- the people interface.

*Pacing*

Perhaps the most important potential constraint is that learning materials contain a pacing structure. The degree and specificity of the pacing varies, but at the least the learning will be cut up into 'chunks' by the use of sections or chapters. How will you use these chunks within your programme structure? Any assessment will have to be timetabled to relate to the chunks, as will any group sessions. A simple example will illustrate some of the problems: in 1992 the OU published a course called *Roles and Relationships; Perspectives on Practice in Health and Welfare* (OU 1992); the course consists of three workbooks and four audiotapes. In order to use it as part of a modular pre-registration nursing course that incorporated both conventional and open learning modes of delivery it was essential to fit the learning into a 15-week module. Most obviously 5 weeks could be assigned to each workbook and a group session scheduled at the end of each, but that assumed that students would find each workbook uniformly easy. However, as Workbook 3 dealt with issues of theory and practice it was felt that the students might need more time for study. Assessment took place in week 15 so it was also important to ensure that Workbook 3 and any associated group work was finished before then. The pacing of *Roles and Relationships* was solved relatively easily, in part because there was no specific reference in the text to the timing of group work – indeed there was no assumption that it would happen at all – so there was freedom to impose another pacing structure. But, in contrast, consider the use of *A Systematic Approach to Nursing Care* (OU 1989), in which the workbooks refer to eight group sessions, each based around a video. The video is itself carefully divided into sections for showing at each group session. While this structure works very well when using the material for unassessed staff development, it is less easy to incorporate into a set modular structure. There are no simple solutions for these problems, but in general it is sensible to retain as much of the original pacing as possible rather than attempt to impose a completely new structure. For example, a learning structure based on eight group sessions can be incorporated into a 15-week module by having a 'two weeks on – two weeks off' schedule.

### Resourcing

Two questions need to be asked here:

- what resources are needed to support the materials?;
- what local resources are available that might enhance the materials?

Most learning materials indicate fairly clearly many of the additional resources the learner needs. Sometimes this is implicit: audiotapes clearly require an audiotape player; sometimes it is explicit as when an activity specifies the use of a library. These resources need to be listed and decisions taken about who will supply them and how. It may be reasonable to assume that all learners can readily access an audiotape player but less reasonable to assume access to a videoplayer. Such assumptions may vary according to the type of learner. However, some of the needs generated by materials are not specified, such as staff development for the teachers who are going to support the programme. While we can assume that teachers are reasonably expert in the general field, they may have problems with particular parts of the material. An example would be *Health and Disease* (OU 1994), a set of learning materials that most health-care teachers could easily support in tutorials. However, because the course includes both biological science and social science perspectives some teachers experience difficulties with the perspective they are less familiar with. The inclusion of some work on epidemiology also poses a challenge to the less numerate! Staff development or staff support can readily resolve such problems but the curriculum needs to show how they are dealt with.

Some locally available resources may not be strictly necessary at all but could add particular value to the programme. Taking as an example the open learning component of a master's degree based on workbooks from Australia (University of South Australia 1993), the teacher used one of the group sessions supporting the material on qualitative research methods to present some current research work using audiotape and videotape and to give the students some experience of working with that type of data. This experience was not strictly necessary for the course but the teacher took the opportunity of offering something extra to challenge and motivate the students. Such opportunities are very likely to occur in relation to clinical work. Few open learning materials – even those specifically designed for health-care practitioners – assume access to particular sorts of clinical experience. This is because they are designed for a mass market that is unpredictable in detail. But health-care teachers

know what clinical experiences are available locally and can add significantly to any course by using such experiences creatively; perhaps through
student visits to a clinical site or input from clinical staff, but also through
the use of records, pictures, and video-recordings.

## The people interface

What support do the materials need from teachers, mentors and administrators? Much will depend on the decisions made about what degree
of open learning the course team aimed for, which will reflect in turn
definitions of studentship and the available resources. Chapters 3 and 6
look in much more detail at the kinds of roles teachers can adopt in open
learning, and teachers can interface the materials and mentors and others
in very many ways. However, the basic planning strategy is to map all
the needs of the learner and to consider how many of them are met by
the materials. What is left out will need to be provided through additional
action; either the materials will need enhancement or adaptation (the
teacher works with the materials) or the learner needs additional services
(the teacher/mentor/administrator works with the learner). The basic
map will be the course aims (or objectives or outcomes) but much of the
guidance role in teaching is so intuitive, so buried within the whole
teaching role, that it is sometimes difficult to bring it into the mapping
process. Figure 2.1 is taken from a very useful article on the guidance
role in relation to open learning. You may not need to consider all of
these in your programme but it may serve as a useful checklist. It is
important not to assume that guidance must be 'people work' as much
may already be contained in the materials – learning management skills,
for example.

Once it has been decided what 'people input' is needed, the detailed
planning can be considered, such as what form the input should take
and how it should be scheduled. The answers to such questions must
differ in each programme, but it is important to make sure that they are
compatible with the basic aims of the programme. For example, if open
learning is being used in order to recruit from a wide geographical area,
then the provision of guidance in one centre open only between 9 am
and 5 pm will disenfranchise many students. However, creative use can
be made of the telephone and increasingly, of computer links. Alternatively, schemes like the DLC diploma schemes and the *Nursing Times*
enrolled-nurse programme make use of resources local to the students,
and it may be possible to do this on a smaller scale, for example, by
helping learners negotiate access to a local library.

Issues around the choice and adaptation of the materials are deal with
in Chapters 4 and 5.

**Figure 2.1**   Defining the tutor role in open learning

|  | Student needs | Scheme provision | |
|---|---|---|---|
| Pre-entry | Clarification of objectives | *Possibilities* | Tutor *may* |
|  | educational | Counselling (face-to-face, | have role at |
|  | vocational | telephone, letter) | pre-entry |
|  | personal | Self-assessment packs/ |  |
|  | Assessment of existing | profiles |  |
|  | skills, knowledge, | Self-diagnostic materials |  |
|  | competencies | Information on courses |  |
|  | Diagnosis of what skills, | (leaflets, database) |  |
|  | etc., need to be acquired | Links to advisory services |  |
|  | Review of learning options | outside scheme |  |
|  | (routes, modes, pace, | Group sessions for |  |
|  | place) | applicants |  |
|  | Clarification of practical |  |  |
|  | issues (cost, funding, |  |  |
|  | time) |  |  |
|  | Confidence building, |  |  |
|  | support, orientation to |  |  |
|  | study |  |  |
| In-course | Induction to open learning | Induction packs | Tutor has key |
|  | Study skills; writing skills, | Study skills packages/ | role in |
|  | numeracy, time | group sessions | meeting |
|  | management, using | Mentor scheme | some/all |
|  | libraries/databases, | Subject specialists | needs |
|  | learning from | Counselling (group or |  |
|  | technology, group skills | individual) |  |
|  | Design of individualized | Negotiation practice work/ |  |
|  | curriculum (modules, | projects |  |
|  | timetable) | Correspondence tutoring |  |
|  | Course/package | Peer assessment |  |
|  | Support structure/help | Norm-referenced/ |  |
|  | with blocks | competence-based tests |  |
|  | Practical work | Progress reviews |  |
|  | Feedback on progress |  |  |
|  | Formal assessment |  |  |
| Exit | Review of progress made | End-of-course review | Tutor's role |
|  | towards objective | Career counselling/referral | may vary |
|  | Certification | to specialists |  |
|  | Career advice | Action planning |  |
|  | Clarification of further |  |  |
|  | objectives |  |  |

*Source*: Reproduced by permission of Blackwell Scientific Publications from Bailey, D. (1992) Facilitator not teacher: a role change for tutors in open learning nursing education, *Journal of Advanced Nursing*, 17, 983–91.

**Students' issues**

As open learning is concerned with enhancing opportunities for student choice, then the curriculum should address the issue of choice in all possible places. In what parts of the curriculum can students make choices? Lewis and Spencer (1986) categorized students' choices as follows:

- whether or not to learn;
- what to learn;
- how to learn (methods, media, route);
- where to learn (the place . . .);
- when to learn (start, finish, pace . . .);
- who to turn to for help (tutors, friends, colleagues . . .);
- how to get learning assessed (and the nature of feedback . . .);
- what to do next.

These individual headings can be brought together as three main issues:

- the purpose of learning;
- the process of learning;
- getting support for learning;

A constant theme in any discussion of open learning should be how and why student motivation is managed. Exploring student motivation has been a consistent focus in open learning because many courses have higher 'drop-out' rates than conventional courses. Within nursing education in the USA, Billings considered that 'Attrition rates from correspondence courses have ranged from 10% to 70% . . . and remains the most serious problem of correspondence instruction' (Billings 1987: 744). Attrition rates of open learning students need to be placed in the context of the open student-entry systems operating in many programmes. There is still concern that some students would not have dropped out if things had been done differently – entry had been more selective, for example, or more support had been given.

*The purpose of learning*

Why do students undertake courses? Those who have mainly worked within pre-registration health-care courses may be less familiar with this as a contentious issue than other teachers because one of the course goals – registration as a practitioner – has overshadowed other debates about aims and goals. The motivation has in part been 'built-in' to the course programme through the introduction of an all-or-nothing 'threshold' or 'gate'. However, those involved with post-registration, in-service, or enhancement education – are more familiar with the practitioner, and her employer, needing to explore the benefits and costs of an educational programme. Qualified practitioners and their employers may be investing heavily in a course and will want sensible and coherent answers to the questions, 'why should I learn?', 'why should I do this course?', and 'what are the benefits to the organization?'

The introduction of open learning greatly reinforces the need for clear course goals and outcomes because it changes education from being a scarce commodity to a more freely available one. The possible effects of this have not yet been fully explored, and indeed may never be realized within health-care education because of the limitations of practice placements. However, any change in the direction of open access will have a profound effect. Many of the routines of educational practice, particularly student selection, are founded on the notion that education is a scarce resource and therefore those admitted to it must be those most able to benefit from it; they should be suitably grateful for their admission and feel appropriately subservient, and once they have completed it they can feel appropriately superior. Education has been a route to an elitist position and has therefore not seriously had to engage in 'selling' its attractions.

The most obvious illustration of a change towards unlimited access is the Open University course P553 *A Systematic Approach to Nursing Care* (OU 1989). First published in 1984 and updated in 1989, the course, which consists of a substantial interactive text and an accompanying video to support group work, has been accessed by many thousands of nurses. Many organizations have used it in formal in-house training courses, but it is also on open sale to any nurse (or anybody else) who wants it. While this course did not originally carry any credit, a computer marked assignment (CMA) was later introduced and a Certificate of Course Completion is now available to successful students. Access to courses has been extended even more widely through the use of popular nursing journals – both *Nursing Times* and *Nursing Standard* now include open learning materials, and the *Nursing Standard* course is supported by television broadcasts. An open learning course in nursing is therefore available in small cheap 'chunks' in every newsagent. If HEIs are going to continue to recruit students – especially students paying full-cost fees – they are going to have to be very clear about what they are selling and why. The 'value-added' by formal registration with a university or college will need to be considered carefully. In the past the ability to offer formal qualifications and credit may have been a decisive factor in attracting students to register and attend classes, but the increasing use of portfolios of work as evidence of learning within Accreditation of Prior Experiential Learning (APEL) schemes may also alter the balance in favour of the student and away from formal institutions. Both of the journal-based courses mentioned above also offer the possibility of participating in assessment and gaining nationally recognized credits (in conjunction with HEIs but not through attendance or necessarily any direct association between the students and the institution).

One of the most obvious ways in which scarcity of education is manifested within the curriculum is in the recruitment phase. Conventionally, students are tested, either through consideration of their experience and qualifications and/or through interview, so that the course places can be filled by the students most likely to succeed. Sponsoring organizations also have a say in supporting those who needed the training, but both are agreed that selection is essential. But if places on a course are no longer a scarce resource, because the use of easily reproducible learning materials removes staffing and accommodation constraints, then the justification for selection is removed. Why should there not be open entry? One remaining argument is that students should not be allowed to enter if they are likely to fail. But this supposes first, that we can accurately predict who is likely to fail, and second, that 'failure' is a negative experience to be avoided at all costs. The concept of 'failure' may itself be linked to the idea of restricted access to opportunity; in a conventional course your 'place' will be given to someone else. In an open learning mode it may be translated into 'I learnt a great deal but have not yet reached the required outcome of the learning', or 'found that I am not able to learn this yet but will do some more preparatory work and then come back to it', but the 'place' may remain available for whenever the learner wants to recommence. So the purpose of an admissions process may become less to allow the institution to select and more to help the student think through her learning needs and resources and try to match them against the course. This reorientation of the admissions process might also imply that it should be divorced from a direct connection with the course or indeed the recruiting HEI; learners, now transformed into consumers, may increasingly seek more impartial advice.

One of the reasons students will continue to use formal educational institutions is that the learning process contained within learning materials is enhanced. HEIs can offer access to specific learning resources, such as computers, books and journals, or to a group of peers. They can offer to enhance the student's motivation through setting timetables and schedules and, in the jargon of the OU, assessment 'cut-off' points. These are not trivial things to offer as anyone who has tried to study alone will readily admit. We suspect that we are not alone in making resolutions to study Ancient Greek or flower arranging or French conversation and finding ourselves wanting in sufficient self-discipline. Health-care practitioners have the added incentive of wanting to improve the care they give, but even so, they lead busy lives and experience competing demands on their time. As was noted in the last chapter, open learning may offer them increased access based on the use of learning materials *plus* some of the motivational aspects of conventional education. The next section will look at some of the ways this can be done.

## The process of learning

In considering the process of learning the curriculum designer has to be most concerned with whether the students are prepared for open learning as a mode of study. This is obviously a most important question, but it is not an easy one to answer. A common perception is that mature students can cope with open learning but '18 year olds' cannot. However, this stereotype cannot be sustained. First, because many primary and secondary schools are now making extensive use of open learning 'type' activities based on resource packs, and younger learners may therefore have considerable experience of independent learning. Second, mature learners may be most familiar with the 'talk-and-chalk' approach and may be very unfamiliar with ideas about student-centred learning. Stereotypes of learners are not therefore useful guides to planning, and student information materials should spell out in considerable detail both the benefits and costs of open learning and what is expected of the learner and the teacher. This may also form the content of an early group meeting, but it would need to happen before the learners began to engage with the materials.

One of the things with which students need help is focusing on the central learning experience. Unlike conventional courses, in which the central experience involves listening to and talking with the teacher, the central experience within open learning is dialogue with the learning materials. This is not to say that teachers will not be helpful or supportive, or indeed inspirational. But if the student cannot cope with the learning materials then the key learning experiences will not happen. The method of dealing with the materials will depend on the medium involved, but the key concept to pursue is that of *active study*. Perhaps this can be best illustrated by contrasting the reading of a book with the reading of text-based learning materials. The important point here is that the curriculum must specify where and how the student will be inducted into the media to be used and the concept of active study. A validator should ask, 'How do you assure yourselves that each student understands the role of the open learning materials?' followed by, 'What processes do you have in place to help the learner with no experience of open learning?' It is important to remember that, while many learners may have experience of one or more open learning systems, the knowledge they have gained may not translate readily into *your* system, and they may not have thought through in any reflective way how an open learning system should work. Remember that many teachers in HE have experience of open learning from working as OU tutors but they find it difficult to use that experience within their routine jobs. Experience may need to be revealed and explored in order to be useful.

### How much choice for the student?

In the open learning mode students should be clear about their choices, but in many courses their choices are highly constrained. These constraints are sometimes simply the product of tradition – that is, the way things needed to be in conventional courses – and these can be opened up. Other constraints may be the product of cost: for example, while ideally we might want to offer the students a choice of the medium in which they study (text, video, etc.) few courses exist in alternative modes and the in-house cost of translation between modes may be too high to make it a practical proposition.

The supposed 'trade-off' between maximizing student control and offering enough framework to support continued motivation and performance is a contentious topic in open learning. The OU undergraduate programme, for example, is highly structured and student progress is largely directed through paced assignments with non-negotiable 'cut-off' dates. Thus some of the possible student control over the logistical trilogy of 'time, pace and place' is removed, and the emphasis remains on place, which is largely uncontentious because it moves a range of costs from the University to the individual. For some learners, this formal structure and lack of choice will assist in getting them through the course; for others it is a tedious imposition. While it can be possible to justify constraints in terms of learner motivation, it might be useful to spell these out and to develop a strategy for testing the precise degree of structure which will yield maximum returns to the learner. A structure oriented to the needs of each student could be operationalized through the use of learning contracts.

The removal of structure leads to considerable logistical challenges to the organization. Take, as an example, the handling of assignments; if students can do their 'set' of assignments at any time then staff contracts or work schedules will need to accommodate unpredictability (although experience of running the course may eventually indicate a stable pattern). More seriously, it might limit the amount of feedback offered if there was any comparability in the assignments done. The OU pattern, where all students answer the same limited menu of questions, would certainly lead to problems of plagiarism if scheduling was abandoned. However, other institutions might be able to develop more practice-focused questions in which each student's response to the assignment was unique. Markers would need to use a criterion rather than a norm-referencing system if assignments were submitted individually. Assessment is just one example of how the effects of increasing (or decreasing) openness need to be carefully thought through in the curriculum planning process.

### Getting support for learning

Open learning has provided a fertile arena for the development of a range of student-support processes. While the teacher or course manager of a conventional course has taken on a range of support duties without any careful exposition of the different roles, within open learning discussion of how different people can take on and combine the necessary roles has been considerable. There are two relationships to be considered within any open learning programme, and three within health-care open learning programmes. These are:

• the teacher and the learner;
• the learner and her peers;
• the teacher, the learner, and her mentor.

In all cases there is an additional 'member' of the team – the learning materials.

### The teacher and the learner

Openness increases student autonomy, but need not mean student isolation. The contact time between teacher and student will be reduced, but the quality of the interaction need not be diminished. The quality of the interaction sustained between a teacher and 250 learners in a lecture theatre for 2 hours for each week of, say, a 15-week semester, is not one which is easily defensible as a major learning experience. Within open learning, the teacher has a different role; she is not the owner of the knowledge, but a partner on the road of discovery.

In terms of the curriculum, the relationship between learner and teacher needs to be clearly spelt out: How often will they meet? How can the learner contact the tutor? What instructions has the learner been given about contacting the learner? What is the principal medium of contact? Because the learner and teacher will not meet routinely week by week there is a need to construct their relationship more carefully and precisely. While this precision about access may be an irritant to the more forthcoming learner who enjoys being able to knock on the teacher's door and get an instant response, it may advantage the less secure learner who would otherwise hesitate to 'bother' the teacher. Knowing that the teacher can be contacted by telephone between 2 pm and 4 pm on Tuesdays and Thursdays gives learners more power than knowing that, as in many conventional courses, they can contact the teacher 'at any time', which often means 'at any time that they are in and it is convenient'. Clearly the notion of the teacher/learner relationship 'rings bells' for the health-care students, and it is well worth spending at least one of the face-to-face sessions exploring the parallels between the teacher/learner contract and the practitioner/client one.

## The learner and her peers

Proponents of open learning have perhaps been the most vociferous in supporting the idea that learners need support from 'ordinary people' as well as from their teachers. This category includes both those that support them through all the vicissitudes of life – family, friends and relatives – as well as those who are linked to them solely by the learning experience – peer learners, mentors and supervisors. However, it is noticeable that much of the advice does not take into account the cultural diversity of the learners. We need to be very careful about suggesting that learners meet in the pub, for example, because of cultural preferences. However, within health-care education we also need to be alert to the different grades, status and experience of our learner groups. Lay experience of raising a child with a major handicap and the perspective of the relevant health-care workers may not sit comfortably together in a learning situation. But this is most emphatically not an argument for not mixing disparate groups, but a comment on what to expect when you do. When any disparate group is required to sit still and listen to a lecture then probably little disruption can occur; when they are given the learning materials and ask to come back later and discuss them, then more controversy should be expected. We consider the fact that learners are prepared for discussion and debate by the learning materials before the 'face-to-face' encounters to be an advantage, but it demands a great deal of the teachers.

## The teacher, the learner and the mentor

We have indicated before that, while conventional education may centre on the dyadic experience (teacher[s]–learner[s]), open learning offers a triadic experience (teacher[s]–materials–learner[s]). However, this characterization ignores the central role within health-care education of the practitioner, acting as mentor/supervisor/teacher – the names and roles change slightly but the central purpose remains the same. This purpose is the exposition and interpretation of the role of the practitioner – usually through acting as a role model. So we are in effect advocating a move, not from dyadic to triadic but from the triadic role to the quadratic role(!): the terminology is obviously unimportant; our question here is how the use of open learning materials might inhibit or enhance the role of the expert practitioner in the learning process.

We have two proposals to make. The first is that learning materials can enhance the relationship between the expert practitioner (whom we will call the mentor) and the rest of the learning 'team'. The second is that we have got a very long way to go in making the best use of the possibilities of open learning in this arena. Consider the role of the mentor in a conventional course: she will attend seminars about the course that her 'mentees' are on, she will be briefed (to varying degrees) about their learning needs, she will be encouraged to contact the teaching team or a particular 'linked teacher' if things go wrong. All of this holds true within the open learning programme. However, in addition, she has a copy of the learning materials used in the course; she thereby has direct access to the learning experience of her 'mentee' and of the central syllabus. She no longer has to rely on 'second-hand' briefings; she can access the learning materials as well as anyone and can structure her input accordingly. The conventional power relationship between teacher and practice mentor is therefore potentially changed, no longer is the latter dependent on the former. Any competent mentor, reading a set of learning materials related to health-care practice, could propose a set of instances or examples that would reinforce or challenge the text. As with any conventional course, she can choose to make nonsense of or to support the central philosophy, but at least she will not fall into a negative position because of lack of knowledge about the teaching content and style. Direct access to the learning materials (because they are freely available in a physical form and are not ephemeral) will also remove the learner from the role of broker: 'In class we talked about death in the following terms: . . . what do you think about it?' Within an open learning programme, in contrast, learner/mentee and mentor can tackle learning together, both assimilating and confronting the learning materials directly.

However, the development of the principles of open learning within practice has only just begun. Ideas within the open learning literature about learners, teachers and mentors being linked by computer technology have not been properly worked through. There is considerable potential for the exploitation of health-service IT systems to enhance the connection between practitioners, learners and HEI-based teachers but it is not yet fully developed. Nevertheless, the potential is there; at the simplest level practice-based learners and mentors can be linked with HEI-based teachers via systems such as E-mail. In addition, software exists that can support text-based dialogue via computer between learners (and mediated by teachers) scattered among a hundred practice sites. This might look like a diversion from our central interest in the introduction of open learning, but, of course, it is intimately connected; teaching is about communication above all, and technology is increasingly available to support rapid communication over distance between individuals and groups.

## The student career

Bailey (1992) has developed a precise schema of student needs, using the concept of a career (see Fig. 2.1). She has mapped some possible course provision against each of the 'learning career' stages of pre-entry, in-course and exit, and we will say more about how each of these might be developed in Chapters 5 and 6. An open learning curriculum needs to specify which aspects of learners' needs are being addressed and through what processes, and Bailey's schema forms a useful structure to ensure that no aspects are missed.

## Teachers' issues

If the learning materials and fellow students are responsible for much of the students' learning, what then is the role of the teacher? When open learning was first introduced within nursing education there was considerable concern that it might threaten both the role of the tutor and indeed their employment! Time has allowed a calmer view to prevail and most arguments for open learning emphasize the potential for an increase in the studentship rather than a decrease in the numbers of faculty. Nowhere is this illustrated more forcibly than in the case of the nursing second- to first-level conversion courses; to cite just one example, a full-time conventional course offered annually for 10 students now has 40 part-time students on an open learning version. The same two teachers still spend much of their time on the course, but within the open learning version the access to education has been increased four-fold for approximately the same educational funding. As the open learning version of the course allows learners to continue to work in their own practice areas, the saving to the service is considerable.

Nevertheless, with open learning, the role of the teacher will change substantially. This forms the substantive content of Chapter 3, but we can summarize the issues here. Perhaps the clearest statement of the argument has been made by Bailey in an article entitled 'Facilitator not teacher: a role change for tutors in open learning nursing education', in which she argues: 'Differences in approach can be clustered around the topics of: the locus of control; learning methodology; the learning context and media; and the curriculum' (Bailey 1992: 983). However, Bailey's argument assumes a more structured teaching role than is probably the case within nursing or para-medical education and therefore a greater degree of necessary change. Most health-care teachers have thought through in some detail the facilitative role and have seen and used the connections between the parallel relationship between teacher and learner and practitioner and client. Nevertheless, Bailey argues that the use of learning materials allows the extension of the facilitative role: 'In many ways, open learning aligns the tutor more closely with the student, away from the institution – though the shift may be mainly psychological and perceptual' (Bailey 1992: 990).

This may be most obviously true of systems in which the tutor is not a member of the central staff team and has an institutionally marginalized role, as in the OU and the DLC Diploma in Nursing programme. However, in the psychological sense it can be realized in many schemes as both the learner and the teacher can address the potential of the learning materials as 'outsiders'. The teacher has no need to 'defend' or 'justify' the choice of substantive content, the example, or the philosophy of the 'text', and can see her role more clearly as guiding the learner along the path or paths necessary to reach her goal. In this guidance role, there may be space for the teacher to enhance the degree of individualization open to the learner. An obvious example familiar to most OU tutors is the advice 'Yes, you can skip what you can't cope with', but within health-care education we can also add 'This part of the course is probably less important for you in your current practice area'. Most learners will do it anyway, but some need permission to begin to deviate from the established path.

### Course administration

Most validation documents have a section related to course management, but administration forms only a small part of that discussion. Probably this avoidance is misplaced for all courses, but open learning poses administrators with particular challenges. These stem largely from two sources – size and non-contiguity. First, open learning courses *may* have larger numbers of students than conventional courses, and learners *may* be studying in a number of different patterns. Simply keeping track of who they are and what they are doing poses problems and record keeping must be precise. The second factor, which exacerbates the first, is that teachers and learners will meet less frequently and the conventional channels of routine communication are therefore closed.

In a conventional course, the teacher may take over a number of administrative tasks – establishing the number of students, for example, giving out handouts, and taking in assignments. As a programme moves away from frequent scheduled contact these roles will have to be organized differently. Instructions or guidelines due to be passed to the students on a particular date may have to be sent via post or telephone, and the administrative systems involved will need to be robust. Whether these tasks remain the responsibility of a teacher or are passed to an administrator is a decision for each institution to make. The point to be made here is that such systems must work well or both the student and the institution might suffer. The student may miss out on essential elements of the course, and not only will considerable energy be spent on remedial action but also the institution leaves itself vulnerable to appeal. In these days of student charters it may be useful to specify quite precisely how and when the open learning student will interface with the organization. The 'up-side' of this problem is that open learners are often good at reading communications sent to them and responding to them. The open learning culture is more likely to be written than verbal, but within a mixed-mode institution it may be possible to combine the best of both.

A variety of accounting mechanisms can be developed depending on need. OU teachers will be familiar with the student contact log that they are required to keep, which demands that they record each contact with the student whether by phone or face to face. This is clearly administrative work but subsumed by the teacher. In a mixed-mode institution students may be 'logged' in other ways, for example, through routine contact with the personal tutor or through attendance at tutorials. Within the OU the despatch of materials is undertaken by the central administration, whereas within an integrated institution this may be a task that is devolved to the teachers who structure it as part of a 'getting to know the materials and the course and the teacher' session.

## Quality assurance

We have looked at how to define quality; here we are concerned with how that definition can underwrite the quality assurance process. There are essentially two approaches to assuring quality in open learning. The first, is to pursue those quality assurance mechanisms that operate for any educational programme, that is, to attend to the *ordinariness* of open learning which is, after all, essentially just another way of delivering education. The second approach is to attend to the *extraordinariness* of open learning, that, it can be argued, presents any quality assurance system with particular challenges and demands. These challenges and demands arise in part because open learning employs different technologies and delivery systems, and in part because it attempts to redesign the roles of learner and teacher. In other words, the challenges come from both the means – the technology – and the ends – the purpose of the programme. While these two approaches – the ordinary and the extraordinary – might appear to be in conflict, in practice they need to operate together in order that no part of the system is ignored and that none of the straightforward and useful elements of quality assurance is forgotten.

Quality assurance must operate at all levels from the institutional to the course and module, so the following discussion starts with accreditation issues and moves on to look at validation, monitoring and review.

## Accreditation

Accreditation generally refers to the institutional context in which education takes place. Institutions are accredited to do various kinds of things that they have demonstrated they can do. Institutions of higher education are accredited – by the government or by a professional body or both – as institutions capable of delivering high quality higher education. Part of that capability resides in the institutional systems for quality assurance and it is important that the open learning systems should be locked firmly into those systems. Where open learning is being carried on outside of such an institutional umbrella – in an NHS Trust, for example, or a private hospital – then a quality assurance framework for education may not be in place and a system will have to be devised. In these circumstances a product-based or value-based approach might be best.

## Validation

Validation is the process by which any particular course or programme is 'approved', either by the institution in which they are run and/or by a professional body. The process is intended to evaluate the degree to which a proposed course can meet its objectives. Where open learning has been established on the margins of institutions, and is seen to be materials-oriented rather than 'proper teaching', it may be operating outside of a formal validated course structure. While there are examples of excellent open learning schemes operating outside of a validated course structure (see, for example, Green 1989 and Johnston 1989) the risk remains that quality will eventually suffer without a structured review process. Such schemes are often started by committed enthusiastic individuals and the quality resides in them and may not be maintained with new staff in place. Teachers could argue legitimately that validation processes were unreasonably bureaucratic and might damage exactly those elements in the programme that were its strengths – its openness and flexibility. However, in recent years validation and review processes have become much more open and flexible and should accommodate any open learning structure without difficulty.

However, a danger of the validation process is that the validators focus on the materials to the exclusion of other aspects. Validators seem to have a need to 'check out' the learning materials for themselves, however well regarded and well documented the source. How justified is this request from validators? Course teams are not required to role play their entire lecture series so is this a case of double standards? The honest answer is 'Yes, it probably is', but it is an understandable response to the perceived 'danger' of innovation. The sensible course team will respond in three ways. First, they will describe their response to the staff development issues discussed above in order to demonstrate that the team is properly prepared for open learning. Second, they will refer to the known quality of the materials by offering information on the producer and their production quality assurance systems, which should be available from any reputable producer. Third, they will produce, if not the actual learning materials, then examples of the type of materials to be used.

## Monitoring and review

Monitoring and review is the process that takes place once a course or programme is 'up and running'. We check to see that the standards that we have set ourselves – and for which we have been approved – are being achieved and we sort out any problems. Again, the routine systems should be applied – the credibility of open learning depends on the comparability of its output. However, monitoring and review is not usually wholly focused on output but also looks at input and process, and here minor modifications to the system in operation may be necessary. The usual sources of process data may not be available and need to be augmented with other mechanisms. Frequent informal contact with students, for example, may be much reduced within open learning and therefore it needs to be replaced by some other mechanism such as telephone contact. If student questionnaires are used to elicit satisfaction indexes for modules or courses they may need to be reworded both to eliminate irrelevant or misleading questions and to introduce more pertinent questions. Some level of detail may be required to inform policy; for example, it might be important to know whether teachers could be reached by telephone, and if not, to know whether the problem lay with the switchboard, with an administrator taking (or not taking) messages or with the teacher.

The purpose of the monitoring and review system is that changes can be made to improve the course, and this is where it is important to keep the issue of ends and means firmly in mind. Suppose that you've found some problems, you are thinking of what to do about them, and the temptation is to go for tried and tested remedies:

- students say, for example, that they are confused about when the assignments need to be in – so the obvious answer is 'let's give them more tutorial support';
- students say that the learning material is difficult – so we respond by giving them more tutorial support;
- students say they feel isolated – so why not give them more tutorial support?

Each of these proposed solutions is simple and attractive but incompatible with the principles of open learning and a 'knee-jerk' reaction back to the tried and tested (although not necessarily more successful) methodologies of conventional teaching. Boot and Hodgson (1988) refer to this process as the 'drift from openness'.

However, each of the problems listed above also has a solution that *is* congruent with the aims of open learning. For example:

- if students are confused about the timing of Tutor Marked Assignments (TMAs) – then we need to write down the instructions more clearly;
- if students are finding the learning material is difficult – then we need to write additional materials to help with the 'difficult' bits;
- if students complain of feeling isolated – then we need to help them set up a self-help group.

So in altering *means*, it is important to think carefully about *ends* and to recall the original rationale for the programme. Let us consider for a moment two vehicles – a Rolls-Royce motor car and a bus. If we just looked at how they worked mechanically we might well discover the car was superior to the bus in almost every way. However, as soon as we consider what a bus is *for*, we find that, as a mass transit vehicle, the Rolls-Royce car is pretty useless. If you have adopted open learning as a mass education vehicle, then it is important not to start evaluating it as if it were a Rolls-Royce. This argument is particularly true of students who are going to 'fail'. If access is increased then the chances of failure may be increased. But instead of being terrified of that, perhaps we need to consider it more broadly. It is, as they say, better to have loved and lost! Many OU students drop out before the end of their course, but they have enjoyed the learning experience they have had.

It is useful when reviewing the strengths and weaknesses of an open learning course to bear in mind the alternatives – and how would they match up? Is all face-to-face teaching perfect? Are *all* lectures exciting charismatic occasions of discovery and mutual support?

## Peer review

Because quality assurance within higher education depends to a considerable extent on peer review (through external validators and external examiners) open learning programmes may experience particular problems. Just because open learning is innovative, there may be very few people with the experience to make a reasonable judgement about an open learning programme, and there may be insufficient other similar schemes around to generate a 'norm'. Nurse teachers will remember that this is exactly the problem encountered when the first Project 2000 courses were introduced. Some of the issues will be solved by time and experience but there are a number of strategies that could assist the process. First, it is important that health-care specialist teachers take notice of the substantial experience that exists in HE on open learning, both in terms of personnel and in terms of the enormous body of literature that now exists. Joining an experienced open learning organization such as the OU as a part-time tutor will be a valuable personal experience but may also bring skills into the individual's main employing organization. The body of literature on open learning is substantially referenced within this book, but the best general introduction can be found in the journal *Open Learning*. Unfortunately, both these strategies will bring the teacher into contact with specialist open learning institutions rather than mixed mode institutions and some of the information may need to be 'translated' into their situation.

Quality cannot be guaranteed by a recipe. The only recipes that can be recommended relate to the things that need to be evaluated and the ways in which this evaluation can be done. The criteria against which the evaluation is finally done will vary depending on what you are trying to achieve. But it is important to remember that in open learning as in any other creative endeavour people rarely achieve perfection.

## Resourcing the programme

When this section was first envisaged it had the working title 'Costing open learning', in part following the model of Rowntree (1992a), which includes a section 'What does open learning cost?', and the ENB monograph, *Costing Open Learning* (Robinson and Clark 1992), and the reader interested in producing a detailed costing of an open learning programme is recommended to consult those texts. However, the idea of costing suggests a concern about absolute costs – is an open learning programme cheaper than its conventional equivalent? – which precludes discussion of the equally important issue of where the costs reside. It can be suggested that moving to open learning from conventional learning is often not inevitably cheaper, but usually moves the responsibility for resourcing around. Two issues therefore need consideration:

- absolute cost;
- responsibility for the cost.

To the question 'Is open learning cheaper?' the most obvious response is 'cheaper than what?' and this is not merely a facetious question because it is true that within HE very few programmes are accurately costed. Comparisons between open and conventional learning are therefore very difficult to make. However, the purpose of doing a costing may be to demonstrate to a purchaser that the open learning is preferable, and in this context the emphasis might be on the costs *to them* rather than the costs overall.

Having acknowledged that, there is plenty of evidence that in many situations, open learning is a cheaper alternative. Rowntree (1992a) describes a programme in which open learning is considerably cheaper than the conventional alternative. However, almost all the savings come in the non-cash costs section which includes:

• lost productive time at work;
• trainer time;
• use of accommodation/facilities;
• setting up costs.

A number of other industrial examples are cited in Rowntree (1992a), all of them demonstrating the importance of the question: *Where do the costs reside?* Using a model of resourcing which differentiates between:

• producers;
• teachers;
• sponsors;
• learners.

it is possible to track the movement of resources between each category. Within open learning, capital costs replace labour: Rumble (1988) asserts that the development of open learning materials: 'represents a form of capital investment which replaces direct student-teacher contact . . . in essence, capital replaces labour'. And some costs/resources therefore move from the teachers, who were previously both producers *and* deliverers, to the producers of learning materials.

For the open learning developer, the issue may be how to get credited with gains elsewhere in the organization (Rowntree 1992a). These may relate to overt and covert course costs, and also to the outcomes of the course, because the issue for students and sponsors may not be cost, but cost-*effectiveness*. Rowntree, in addressing this issue, cites the results of a survey of open learning in industry:

> The striking conclusion from the survey is that companies' decisions to use OL were usually not explicitly related to costs, despite the indication from the case studies that OL is often substantially cheaper. The most frequent reasons for choosing OL were the logistics of training – because trainees were scattered round the country, on shift work, or difficult to release from their jobs.
>
> (Coopers and Lybrand, cited in Rowntree 1992a: 196)

These conclusions have clear implications for open learning in health care. However, it is important to note that there can never be one model of an open learning programme because the possible variation is too great – just as with conventional programmes. But for those of us who work in dual-mode or integrated institutions the main danger when constructing an open learning curriculum is not that we get it 'wrong' in some indefinable way, but that we revert to the tried and tested conventional solutions. The challenge is to believe that in an open learning programme there should be an open learning solution to any problem. This requires considerable creativity and flexibility, and if open learning is in its infancy in the institution, some courage and stubbornness. It helps to remember that conventional learning is not 'perfect', and that when a learner says, as they will, 'I can't cope with open learning', many learners feel similarly about conventional learning.

# *Three*

# Mapping the teacher's role

What we want to evoke in this chapter is a sense that teaching is a complex role and that the introduction of open learning materials does not make it any less complex but alters the nature of the complexity.

As a teacher you are effectively in the position of presenting a learning package to learners. What you put in it and how you encourage them to unpack it and reconstruct it will have consequences for their learning. As we have already noted, many teachers now use a combination of conventional teaching and open learning methods in order to disseminate learning curricula. Many HEIs are leaning towards a much greater engagement with open learning materials. And changing times of necessity, lead to changing roles for the teacher. Texts on open learning often say something to the effect of 'Do not reteach the materials' (Clark 1989): but if you do not teach the materials then what do you do? A negative injunction is not helpful in thinking through what positive actions you might take. The adjustment of the teacher role is therefore crucial to the successful use of open learning materials within an institutional setting, and this chapter raises a series of issues that are intended to open up possibilities for a reconstituted teacher role. Earlier chapters have already outlined some of the ways in which teacher, learners and institutions may be affected by open learning. It has been noted that the use of open learning materials needs to be built on sound curriculum planning and to be delivered with an effective system of monitoring, review and evaluation. And good curriculum planning and sensitive evaluation are necessary whatever the context of learning. However, this chapter stands back and looks at how the 'stage' for learning is created, at the implications of who the 'players' are, and at some of the 'props' that can aid the adequate performance of learning. If, in any teaching programme the curriculum can be seen as the 'script', then this chapter takes a look at the overall components that shape how the script can be 'directed'.

Dramaturgical imagery has been much used in micro-sociology and often provides a useful way to look at how individuals relate to each other (see, for example, much of Goffman's work, and particularly *Presentation of Self in Everyday Life* 1959). In this chapter dramaturgy is not being used in a rigorous sociological way but as a metaphor to assist the understanding of the complexities of the teacher's multiple role.

## Setting the stage

To take this analogy one stage further: one option that follows from having a script is learning to play a part. A curriculum with a basis in practice is in some senses offering learners roles to play – one of the foremost of these is how to be a good practitioner, whether this is being a good practitioner in terms of wound care, or care of older people. Thus in learning programmes learners consider the script for good practice and by implication how to engage in good practice. In the classroom dealing with the script is rehearsing for being out there playing the part for real. It is important then for the teacher to consider how well the script maps on to the real-life situation that learners may eventually face. If the learning set is all about the tender loving care of frail older people and steeped in deep discussion about the meaning of integrity, autonomy and dignity, all admirable concepts in themselves: then learners are going to find themselves somewhat thrown when they go on night duty with one other person and 24 frail older people of whom 13 are dementing. A good curriculum (script) will acknowledge the reality of practice. A good teacher will reinforce the script, helping learners to consider different interpretations of it and to understand its nuances. She will present 'props' that will help learners understand better how to see the script, she will share her own understanding.

The teacher who uses open learning materials has a multiple role that is overall a very rich one. But of what does this multiple role consist? Clark observes:

> the key role of the teacher is no longer that of information transmitter when open learning materials are being used, but rather that of facilitator; the need to stimulate and support students becomes their most vital function.
>
> (Clark 1989: 178)

Other writers too, have remarked on the alteration and consequent diversity of teaching tasks that confront teachers who become involved with open learning (Clarke *et al.* 1986; Bailey 1987, 1992). There is agreement that the role takes on new dimensions, understating some conventional aspects of the teacher's role and emphasizing aspects that had hitherto been marginal. This can be a challenging process. As Gilliard remarks:

> There is an assumption, not necessarily shared by distance educators themselves, but prevalent among those who work in or who are affected in some way by the education system, that distance education is an inferior form of teaching and learning. In this view it is merely a substitute process maintained for the benefit of those unfortunates who cannot participate in the Real Thing . . . It is a substitute for a learning situation where there is a teacher present who speaks, responds to learners and interacts with them in contiguous time and space.
>
> (Gilliard 1993: 185–6)

And he goes on to suggest that this view privileges teaching and not learning. The implication of this is the privileging of teachers over learners whereas the ideal of many open learning educators is that open learning should privilege the learner. But privileging the learner should not undermine the role of the teacher although it will alter her relationship to the learner.

In the following section we cite a number of roles that the teacher who is involved in open learning may take on. Some relate to the system (whether of the institution or of the health-care setting where practice takes place), some to personnel and some to educational resources. Changes in the role of teacher mean changes in the relationship to the system, personnel and to resources.

In other works on the role of teacher in open learning you may well see the role divided in different ways and different emphases placed on it. Such discussions are a starting point and stimulus for teachers to reflect on their own experiences and to explore the potential for their expertise to be transformed according to their situation, rather than as a formula for how to teach in an open learning situation.

## The teacher's role

Perhaps overall, *manager* is the word that can be used to describe the teacher's new role. Management involves combining personnel, systems and resources to get the job in hand done (see an array of management books for the basic concepts involved in management education (for a summary see Pugh and Hickson 1989)). Each teacher deals with people (learners, practitioners, college personnel, etc.); with systems (the delivery system for the learning, the relationship between her institution and health-care practice settings) and with resources (the open learning materials, other resource materials). Perhaps even more appositely, in terms of the imagery of this chapter the teacher becomes an *actor manager*. The teacher not only deals with the props behind the scene and the systems that get the show on the road but also she is on stage: she performs. The rest of this chapter considers the various elements that 'get the show on the road' bearing in mind that what is being sought as a final product for a mixed-mode learning programme is a 'performance' that works well for everyone who is involved with it. Again as with the imagery of drama and the stage we are not using management in a rigorously defined way but more as an image to help with thinking about handling a number of educationally linked components in one role.

Below are outlined some aspects of the teacher's role that deserve consideration. Some may be specific named roles, i.e. counsellor. Others may be roles that a teacher will move between in one encounter with learners (say mentoring, facilitating and coaching in one session). The balance will depend partly on your institution and how *they* want the 'script' of the curriculum directed and partly on how *you* want it directed.

## The teacher as manager

The role of manager may be highly constrained, for example if an elaborate delivery system is already *in situ*, learning materials have already been chosen and learners already recruited. For example the OU has a complex and comprehensive tutorial system in place; the *Nursing Times* Open Learning Programme has a network of tutors who are closely briefed on its conversion programme. Or it may be a role that can be developed as the teacher goes along. The balance of the management may vary from organization to organization: in some colleges the teacher may be closely involved in developing resources, in others she may be more involved in the setting up of a delivery system, in some she may only be involved at the delivery stage itself. Management of resources at the design stage of a programme involves being both proactive in taking action to put things together but also potentially reactive later so that problems can be ironed out and components rearranged if they do not achieve the desired outcomes. Similarly management of aspects of programme delivery at the design stage may be followed by ironing out difficulties as the system is confronted with real learners. Teachers who are involved in delivery itself will be able to feedback about adjustments that might need to be made. So these aspects of management have a continuing function throughout the life of an open learning programme.

## The teacher as broker

In certain open learning schemes the teacher may become a broker between open learning materials, learners and the practice situation. In Chapter 2 we referred to this as a quadratric role: broker, however seems a bit more manageable! Conventionally in the health-care occupations brokerage functions for teachers were limited perhaps to mediating between learners and practice-placement supervisors. Now materials enter the practice arena too. The teacher weighs up in advance their possible uses and she fosters the links between practice and materials making sure that there is a good fit. She sets up practice situations for learners to go to and rather like an architect she mediates between the work practice setting, the materials and the learners. A broker is in the middle between different interests. Such a role is valuable. The teacher effectively becomes the interface between the various significant components in the learner's education. Her value is that she is able to programme the brokerage in such a way as to provide the best overall environment for the learner(s). One of the most valuable characteristics of good brokerage is that it is disinterested. It is not advancing the claims of one side against another. It involves mediating so that the best results can be obtained.

## The teacher as monitor

Monitoring can be seen as a process whereby the quality of teaching experienced by the students is assessed. The role usually has some official place in an open learning scheme, as checks are made on the extent and quality of teacher's written comments on students' work. One of the most important aspects of monitoring is *recording* assessments of various sorts, so that there are bases for comparisons of the quality of the teaching for various students and possibly so comparisons can be made between years (or presentations). Monitoring the course can provide valuable information for the next presentation and is of course allied to a notion of maintaining the quality of the programme.

Aspects of the student's experience are recorded: most usually as indicators of teacher quality. However, within open learning programmes the monitoring of the student's progress may be an important part of the overall monitoring role. In a conventional course, the absence of any individual student can be readily spotted. With open learning, the absence of the student from her desk at ten o'clock at night, or her inability to sit down at her desk at all may not be nearly so apparent. So it may be important to record key events that indicate her progress, for example a student's telephone enquiry, or a note explaining that she has had flu: something that may not be important in itself but that can act as an indicator. It is not the dog that didn't bark, but the student who didn't phone that can prove a valuable clue to how someone is getting on. In open learning it is a matter of finding the equivalent of the student who is absent from class.

For the learner, the teacher may well be the only person with whom she has contact within the institution. Indeed for some learners the teacher may 'become' the institution. So it is very important that the communication from teacher to learner is clear, concise and usable. Monitoring within an open learning situation, then, is quite a public activity. As with open learning in general there seems to be a paradox. While the students largely speaking learns privately in her own environment, the materials are very public. And while the teacher may comment on a student's work privately on a one-to-one basis, monitoring again makes it a public activity.

### The teacher as researcher

This role is not necessarily that of researcher with a big R although some teachers may wish to consider doing research. The research role involves the constant probing and searching for answers to questions that come up during the course of the dissemination of the learning programme and in practice situations. Even in commonplace situations of meetings between teacher and student there are questions that the teacher may wish to ask herself about what is going on: Why are learners not asking questions? Why are learners only asking questions about certain aspects of the course? Why are some learners asking questions and other learners remaining silent?

In open learning the questions to ask may be different from those asked in classroom situations: Why do certain diagrams always cause trouble? Why are some learners unable to write evaluative comments in response to activities? Why do some students find the in-depth reading of text so difficult? To see such issues as problems in the research sense (rather than in the annoyance sense) really creates an essential link with monitoring but goes one step further and asks the question 'why?' The answering of such questions may turn out to be important at a number of levels: to help individual students but also teachers may be called upon to design amendments to the open learning materials themselves or to work with others in redesigning the curriculum.

### The teacher as mentor

The role of mentor is nowadays quite often a named role for the teacher (and in some learning programmes the mentor role may also be used in terms of an experienced practitioner working with a learner practitioner). In this book we are leaving aside formal definitions as made by different occupations and focusing on what we believe to be the primary purpose of most mentoring activity. The role calls upon the teacher to develop some kind of special relationship with the individual learner and to make her expertise and experiences available to the learner as a kind of filter through which the learning may be fostered. In a sense it is making available to the learner how to act a part. The teacher is able to explain why and how she does things in certain circumstances and to demonstrate to the learner how she would use her own expertise in circumstances in which the learner finds herself.

In her relationship with the student the mentor has the materials as an important way of negotiating the relationship. She and the student together can explore how the materials reflect the practice situation and if there are other areas they need to deal with, not covered by the materials. The mentor can also leave the student with open learning materials that can be seen as a surrogate: after all she cannot be with the student all the time.

Almost by definition a teacher cannot act as mentor to very many learners because it is a personal and labour-intensive role. So if there is a large intake of students who are going to do an open learning course then the allocation of a considerable number of mentors may be required.

### The teacher as counsellor

When open learning educators use the word counsellor they tend to use it in the sense of educational counselling:

> Adults, studying full time or part time, need advice and encouragement on a broader basis than the content of the course that they are studying. Implicitly or explicitly, they ask themselves 'how am I getting on?', 'what are my skills and interests?', 'where might this lead?', 'what shall I study next?'
>
> (Grugeon 1987: 195)

Grugeon places learning more widely in adults' lives with this introductory paragraph to an article on education counselling and open learning by suggesting that people seek advice about where their education is taking them. Clearly guidance in this field will be appreciated by many learners. However educational counselling has other aspects too. Adult learners may not find it very easy to fit in their learning with the other demands on them. For them working on an open learning programme takes place within the context of the rest of their lives. Students who have practice placements may encounter personal difficulties in adjusting or practical difficulties in fitting the practice placements in with other demands on them. Teacher as counsellor is a role that is helping others fit their various roles together so that optimum learning can take place.

In some open learning schemes the roles of teacher and counsellor are put together in the job specification and teachers are referred to as tutor/counsellors or teacher/counsellors.

## The teacher as facilitator

In many discussions of the role of the teacher in open learning, facilitation is seen as the major role that a teacher is likely to take on in an open learning programme (see Clark 1989; Bailey 1992). It means enabling the learner(s) to proceed with their task smoothly and fully. It is enabling people to get the best out of a situation and does not necessarily mean teaching. Open learning materials may present tasks to be done, discussion to be had and it is up to the teacher to facilitate these. Facilitation may be in a group situation or it may be over the telephone or in one-to-one situations. However it is conducted, the emphasis is on enabling. While we would not go as far as saying that you do not even know that a good facilitator is there; a good facilitator *is* someone who does focus on the task at hand and keeps all the extraneous 'noise' as low as possible. Various researchers have noted that even when ostensible transfer has been made from the conventional tutor role to facilitating that some individual tutor/facilitators still talk more than their students (Murgatroyd 1980) and Bailey in her polarization of the teacher/facilitator roles observes that the teacher talks most of the time while the facilitator encourages the learner to talk (Bailey 1992). Nevertheless in a situation when the teacher has but few chances to do face-to-face work with her students the temptation can be overwhelming to talk away nineteen to the dozen to make the best use of the time. But if you are focusing on some kind of an experiential approach then it is crucial that the experiences of students can emerge: and that does require the students to talk.

## The teacher as coach

A teacher may become a coach. There will, of course, be some occasions when the open learning materials do not carry the full range of the learning that is required by the curriculum and the teacher may need to complement this with face-to-face teaching. Teachers may also have people in their groups who are having difficulties learning with the open learning format and they may need additional coaching assistance. Indeed they may have students who are not familiar with study skills at all. And in these circumstances there is a very substantial role for the teacher that may be fulfilled in a number of ways: in face-to-face work, in detailed commentary on written work, in telephone work and in the provision of supplementary reading about study skills. (This links too with the role of counsellor where a teacher might recommend that a student does a local study skills course or a course aimed at helping with particular difficulties such as problems with numeracy.)

Harris notes that in open learning materials the main course often writes for a student who is 'the ideal mature student, challenging, critical, with a certain independence, but still firmly contained within and committed to the framework of the pieces [of open learning materials]': while the student represented in the supplementary materials (i.e. the accompanying study guide, study skills materials and so on) wants to cut corners and has a pragmatic approach (Harris 1987: 108). We might also say that in many study guides the student is seen as a person who will need help to timetable their study, to learn how to 'do' study and so on. The coaching role is one that accommodates both these sides of the student as perceived in the materials since coaching is not only about getting people up to a certain standard (as in the olden days when learners who might fail an exam were given extra coaching) but also helping them aspire to excellence in their field (as, for example, athletic coaches). It can also mean assessing when a period of intensive learning work would be useful for an individual and finding ways of intensifying the experience of open learning (for example with specific extra reading).

### The teacher as translator

Again this role links with some previously discussed. To be a translator involves assisting learners to make sense of the materials. Unless materials are very closely tailored to the needs of one group there will inevitably be points at which it does not fit. The development constraints of a great deal of open learning material (particularly that which has a practice orientation) means that it tends to be either generalist or aimed at one particular practice group or setting. One of the ways in which this happens, for example, is when a piece of learning material has been written for nurses but is potentially very useful to, say, physiotherapists. Many learners are put off by examples about occupational groups other than their own. But using such examples creatively may enable much more learning to be achieved. Another important aspect of the role of translator is to help learners apply overall concepts to local situations. For example to use a course like the OU's *Systematic Approach to Nursing Care* and apply the nursing process into what goes on in a particular clinical arena is to enrich the materials considerably. In much traditional teaching the teacher has managed the learning of the course and books have provided specific examples of taught concepts, in other words the teacher has managed the learning, resource materials have managed the content. But in open learning this idea is turned on its head. For the teacher becomes the translator of the learning into local examples and the materials manage the learning. It is difficult to overemphasize the importance of this contribution of the teacher to open learning. It is perhaps something that Scottish, Welsh and Irish teachers are historically more aware of because of the Anglocentric nature of many research and textbooks (a tradition that unfortunately appears to have been carried forward in some open learning packages). They have always had to fill in the gaps, and apply resource material or open learning materials to Scotland or Wales or Northern Ireland. But it is something that many teachers are bound to become more concerned about as they realize the generalist nature of much of the open learning materials with which they are dealing.

## The teacher as resource

The teacher may herself become a resource for the learners (in addition to controlling or negotiating other resources in an open learning scheme). In some respects this role is rather like the role of mentor except that she may be able to utilize it in a group situation to larger numbers of learners. She herself has information, experience, theoretical standpoints and practice expertise in her own repertoire (see, for example, the practitioner/learner case studies in Schön 1991, and the concept of expert practitioner as expounded by Benner 1984). She can therefore model for the learners how these can be put together. This is particularly important when we consider that a programme based round open learning is a sophisticated phenomenon. Learners need to see that the various threads can be brought together in the context of their own practice. But more than that it is useful for them to be able to see someone going through the programme with them. It is similar to the experience of a good actor, who has the technique, skill and artistry to be able to put on a performance but who is constantly looking at the script to find new ways of expressing herself through it. An actor is always looking for something new in performances with which she is already familiar. And this is true too of the teacher in her role as a resource. She looks at how she can exemplify the points of practice in open learning materials for her learners.

## The teacher as buyer

The teacher may become involved in buying open learning materials. In doing this she is choosing and evaluating for the students. This role is most likely to be one a teacher takes on as a member of a course-development team and in Chapter 2 when we discussed the iterative model we suggested that a number of courses would need to be bought and assessed at the curriculum development stage of preparation. This is not, however, likely to be true of some open learning centres where students come in to browse through the shelves and choose from catalogues. Nevertheless, even where students have choice as in the scheme for enrolled nurses as reported by Johnston (1989), they choose from a very limited range. And where programmes are integrated into valida-tion schemes the choices may be non-existent. In Chapters 4 and 5 we explore some of the issues that are relevant when assessing learning materials.

### The teacher as materials developer

If materials development *is* to be an important component of the role then the institution needs to acknowledge this. As we noted in Chapter 1, it is not always easy to transfer one's attention from wrestling with presenting a written account of conceptual problems to face-to-face teaching: plus the fact that developing open learning materials is a very labour-intensive form of activity. If a teacher finds that her role is likely to involve developing materials she needs to note that, not only does this role bring in its trail a number of materials-development-orientated roles (for example, writer, critical reader, editor, photographic researcher, lay-out designer, negotiator and so on) but it also has substantial implications for the various roles outlined above. To do materials development on the margins of one's time is likely to do that role a disservice. To do mate-rials development more fully will of necessity involve looking at how many of the above roles can still successfully be taken on. We deal with the mechanics of materials development in Chapters 4 and 5 on the assumption that for most teachers it will not be a central component of their teaching role. For any teacher who finds that it is going to be a central component in her role there are a number of excellent texts that explore the process of materials development, notably a series of books by Derek Rowntree (see Bibliography).

### Putting it together

So far then we have described a number of very different roles. Now we begin to look at whether combining them in various ways is significant. The different roles that a teacher can take on have import for various areas in the development and presentation of an open learning pro-gramme. Taking the basic breakdown of the issues of importance to someone with a responsibility for managing the roles might be mapped something as follows (see Fig. 3.1).

If we look at this figure we can suggest different teachers may have their main responsibility located on different parts of the diagram. For example, an overall pastoral responsibility would place emphasis on a role on the left-hand side of the diagram. An emphasis on pedagogic functions would see the emphasis on the bottom right-hand side of the diagram. A managerial responsibility in the strict meaning of the word

**Figure 3.1**

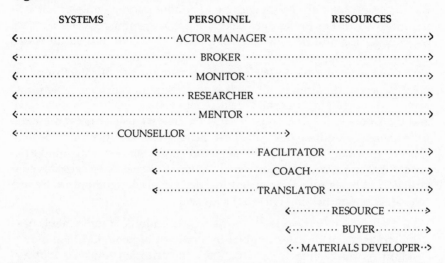

would see a role developed in the top half of the diagram. The more elaborate the open learning scheme the more the various roles might be hived off from each other and invested in separate individuals. In most colleges teachers will probably be expected to take on some aspects of a number of these roles. It can also be seen that some clusters of roles are more orientated to the open learning programme as a whole and to aspects of the relationships between the materials, the people and the delivery system, whereas others focus on systems and people or people and materials. (One role we have not covered, that of course team chair in materials development, is probably the role that most overlaps in relation to systems and resources.) As open learning programmes become more prevalent some teachers will probably find that they are concentrating on one particular cluster of the whole multiple role.

**Reflecting on the role**

So far, we have suggested that there are a multiplicity of roles for teachers to take up if they are going to use open learning materials. In earlier chapters we also noted that there is a multiplicity of possible programmes that involve open learning running from those that are entirely materials-based through to mixed-mode presentations involving open learning and varying amounts of face-to-face contact. Clearly these two threads need to be put together so that a picture is created of what sort of teacher role will be helpful for the various combinations of resources. Now to some extent this is a matter of personal style and taste. For example, it might be suggested that the teacher who is involved in a scheme that involves the wholesale take up of a major open learning package might be thinking more about her brokerage, facilitating and mentor roles rather than those of design and materials development. However, not all decisions on how to develop a cluster of roles are likely to be so straightforward. And what we want to suggest here is a systematic use of something that many teachers do already – which is to engage in reflective practice as a way of considering the relationship between the resources they have and their potential roles. To begin this process we use a quotation taken from some guidelines developed by Schön, whose work on reflective practice is widely known in the personal caring services. The quotation chosen encompasses both courses of action and roles and sees the construction of one's role as a cause for reflection. Talking about the reflective practitioner, Schön (1991: 62) suggests:

> He [*sic*] may reflect on tacit norms which underlie a judgement, or on strategies or theories implicit in a pattern of behaviour. He may reflect on the feeling for a situation which has led him to adopt a particular course of action, on the way he has framed the problem he is trying to solve, or on the role he has constructed for himself within the larger institutional context.

Frances Abraham has simplified this quotation to suggest a checklist for reflection:

- reflection on any tacit or taken for granted norms and appreciations underlying judgements;
- reflections on strategies and theories implicit in a pattern of behaviour;
- reflection on feelings in a situation that suggests a particular course of action;
- reflection on the way a problem is framed;
- reflection on the role constructed by the helper for him or herself within the larger institution.
  (Abraham 1992, cited in Open University 1992, Workbook 1: 38)

### Reflections on any tacit or taken for granted norms and appreciations underlying judgements

By definition, tacit or taken for granted norms are difficult to articulate. Sometimes people are not even aware that they have them. We have already begun to untangle some of the common tacit assumptions that, of necessity, need to be challenged when thinking about the multiple role of teachers in open learning schemes. Perhaps the chief of these is that teaching involves centrally face-to-face work, i.e. that this is the main feature of teaching. In fact teachers have always marked work, prepared curricula, examined and evaluated what they have done. Perhaps the assumption of teaching as being about standing in front of a class is the bit that the public can see: the bit where the teacher *acts out* her role. It is the public aspect of the job. That is probably why open learning makes some teachers nervous: if the public aspect of the job goes then she is left with a role that is not easy to explain to the public!

In conventional teaching, teachers, as it were, work towards a performance, they work towards those contact hours with the learners. And that is, of course, a tacit assumption about the job: that it will at some specific time and in some specific arena be 'consummated'. But certainly if a teacher is, for example, closely involved with materials development then the consummation of the job – the product – is divorced in time and presentation from her role as a materials developer. By the time the product comes on stream she may well be in the middle of developing the next materials development programme. And if the main form of contact with students is in marking their work, again there is a temporal disjunction between the act of teaching or supporting the learning and the reception of this by students. In order to keep the role satisfying it is necessary to be aware of this 'stagger' that exists in open teaching. The payoffs may not be so immediate as they are in conventional teaching. And perhaps that is why so many teachers do continue to find conventional teaching satisfying: it provides instant feedback. However, any understanding of teaching as being about instant contact, feedback and rewards does need to be examined carefully when the role of teacher changes to one in the field of open learning.

Any potential changes in the teacher's role may well also be rendered more difficult by tacit assumptions made by learners about what teachers do. These may be assumptions about teaching and learning and the place that learners play in these processes. They may be tacit assumptions about the nature of open learning. Teachers therefore need to think through how their learners may be thinking about the learning experience. This will, of course, depend on their experience of learning hitherto. A group of student nurses just out of school may have different assumptions from a group of mature learners who have experienced a variety of learning environments. (Although this may be swings and roundabouts: learners just out of school may have been used to a seminar system where they have taken a great deal of responsibility for their learning whereas older learners who have had a wealth of learning environments may nevertheless fail to value these as learning experiences.) The type of teaching and learning that have been dominant in people's past experience will be important. If people consider that teaching is something that is done to them then they will have difficulty in understanding that the learner's role in the learning process can be active.

The teacher's concept of her role whether as a traditional or open learning teacher is not an isolated thing, it *will* be interpreted by learners and they *will* affect the extent to which the teacher is able to play her chosen role (at least to begin with). Some groups of learners may well need educating to a new role themselves. While seen by many as not very productive, chalk and talk is actually very easy for many learners since it takes from them any overt responsibility for doing anything. If a teacher decides to change her role this is certainly something that is socially significant for her learners.

Face-to-face teaching involves some of the tacit assumptions made by learners about their own role and about the teacher's. For example:

- the teacher will keep probing until she has got the answer she wants (the emphasis here being on getting things *right for the teacher* rather than exploring them openly);
- if the teacher has given you a textbook or article to read the ensured way to prosper in writing an assignment is to feed large chunks of this back to her;
- the teacher's role is to stand in front of the class and tell them things, the student's role is to sit and listen;
- people who are forthcoming in tutorial sessions are teacher's pets (proving that some tacit assumptions have a long history and can go back to the early parts of people's childhoods).

Such assumptions are about the management of the learning, content and group process and most teachers almost certainly have their own fund of examples of assumptions that learners make about the role of teacher and student.

### Tacit assumptions about open learning

Open learning has brought its own fund of tacit assumptions too. Some of them translate quite easily from the sorts of assumptions around face-to-face teaching. For example (using an item from the above list as a basis), some open learners think that they need to feed large chunks of the learning materials almost verbatim back to the teacher in their essays. Others are more closely related to the nature of open learning materials themselves. Many people (not just those undertaking open learning courses) believe 'if it is written down it must be right'. There is a strong tradition that anything published must be correct. You can see where this assumption comes from. Academic education has been closely re-lated to text. People have been encouraged (and sometimes forced) to read books throughout their education as being the correct way to absorb knowledge. Thus when an educational programme is largely carried by text it can make it rather difficult to approach that text critically.

Many students respond to examples (for instance examples from a profession other than their own) by dismissing them – 'it's talking about occupational therapists here, that can't have anything to do with me as I'm a nurse'. This tacit assumption is at a first glance quite reasonable. One thing adult learners do is look through material with an eye to its relevance to themselves. And indeed on many occasions this sifting through may be a useful exercise. However, it can also be a sign that students are getting hung up on detail: that is to say that they are not looking for the underlying questions and processes being addressed in the materials. It may also be a product of an idea that 'a book can't be as good as real life' and that the examples from it should therefore be dismissed.

Some students are resentful of material that asks them to engage with their own feelings. And there are good reasons why, for many people this can feel inappropriate, not the least of which is that the team who has written the materials often does not reveal their own feelings. Students feel there is no sense of reciprocity. They feel that they are doing all the giving out and that nothing is coming back their way. The tacit assumption here, however, may be that one's own personal approach to an issue is not valid or relevant. Learners who think this may be puzzled as to why an activity should ask about their experience. But adult learners' experience is an important resource in learning that really everyone needs to capitalize on (see the work of Tough on the extent to which adult learners value their own experience of learning 1981, 1982).

There are a number of taken for granted assumptions around, particularly in the area of practice placements in an open learning programme. While many people think a practice supervisor is absolutely essential, occasionally this arrangement may be problematic. For example, is it better that learners should be closely supervised by someone whose idea of learner support is to shoot questions at them and subject them to stress, or is it better to also support them with open learning materials that help them through their practice? The teacher may not be in control of the practice placements but can certainly complement what happens to learners with supportive open learning materials. Additionally the materials can always be there on a practice placement while supervisors may not (because of holidays, shifts, other courses they have to take and so on).

### Reflection on theories or strategies implicit in a pattern of behaviour

Reflections about tacit assumptions lead into reflections on theories or strategies implicit in a pattern of behaviour and is an important area of reflection in relation to notions of learning both for teacher and students,

Behind people's behaviour and assumptions as learners or teachers are, for example, theories about what learning is and how it should be acted upon. If you look back at some of the tacit assumptions we have suggested above you will see that an underlying 'theory' for many people is that *learning is passive* – sit and listen – absorb information rather than engage in activities – learning is something that comes in rather than goes out (i.e. using your experience is not appropriate, your strategy is to wait to be given your learning). The other side of this coin is that some teachers *tell* people, set up right answers (i.e. learners reach a predetermined level of substantive knowledge – not learn how to think for themselves). For someone to be a passive learner it always helps to have an authoritarian teacher!

There has been an interesting debate within nursing education that suggests that some of the tacit strategies adopted by nurses actually translate into modes of teaching that are not easy to square with open learning programmes. The medical model, in particular, which leaves the patient uninformed but sometimes unrealistically assured is one that can translate into the learner whose performance is not adequately conveyed to her or who receives bland and unhelpful feedback on her work (Lister 1991, cited in Bailey 1992). So strategies about how to 'handle' people educationally also need to be examined to see whether they yield up tacit strategies from other influential areas of life too.

Many learners see activities in open learning text as intrusive. Again there is an underlying theory of learning as a passive phenomenon. People may read all the text and miss out the activities. In an interesting study of learners' attitudes to learning activities in open learning text, Lockwood found that many learners do a cost–benefit analysis of the activities: how many they need to do to help them through the next assignment, how many they can miss out. Many learners appeared to look on activities highly pragmatically (Lockwood 1990). In a personal communication to one of the authors of this book, a teacher testing out OU materials observed, 'Once you get over the OU's little foibles about activities and ignore them the course is very interesting'. Such an approach does mean that people are not relating to the materials as was intended. There are all sorts of ways in which people engage with the activities. These range from following the instructions and doing the whole thing as specified through taking a few minutes to think about what one might answer if one was going to do the activity to ignoring the activities completely. All these strategies indicate tacit assumptions about how to tackle materials and therefore imply what people theorize learning is about. Not doing the activities is not to see the learning as active. Therefore it is as well at the outset to explore with learners how they will tackle the materials, what they think they should be doing with them and so on.

Overall then it is helpful if a teacher coming to the role of teacher in an open learning programme can work out the theories and strategies of her current role and that of her learners. It might be the case that one underlying theory is that face-to-face is best and that other types of learning are inferior to this. Holding on to such a theory does not augur well for adjusting to a new role in an open learning situation.

## *Reflection on feelings in a situation that suggests a particular course of action*

If a teacher reflects both on her own feelings and those of her learners she can begin to fashion more fully the role that she wants to take on in encounters when they meet. A classroom situation, infrequent though it may be in an open learning programme, is one where feelings are likely to be significant. As we noted earlier the group process has to get managed somehow and a teacher may be faced with people who do not have enough confidence to learn, who do not believe in their own ability and who are not yet able to really assess what they themselves can do. In the face of such an array of emotions the teacher's role becomes extremely important. At some point the teacher's role does have to acknowledge learner insecurities whether this is in the classroom, on the telephone or in written comments. How does this relate to taking on learner insecurities in a traditional teaching situation? Will the same approach to feelings be appropriate in the new reconstituted role? And how can the teacher take on learner insecurities if the open learning materials have taken on a broad array of support functions? There are no easy answers to these questions. It is necessary to be alert and to be ready for feelings and insecurities to manifest themselves, perhaps in situations that are not face to face. Feelings can be manifested outside the (sometimes rare) classroom situation, for example, a telephone call by a distraught student; a note attached to an essay, a plea for special circumstances to be taken into account. In response to a telephone call the teacher may really have to do something then and there. Notes and other written communications may give the teacher more time to think how she can be supportive than having to respond to high feelings directly in the classroom.

In terms of the teacher's role the expression of learner's feelings can suggest a course of action or at least provide an opportunity for bringing to the surface one of the multiple roles available. For example, they provide a chance to counsel or suggest that monitoring of a fraught situation may be worthwhile.

In addition it is useful for the teacher to acknowledge that open learning materials can take on the affective domain. Some of them tackle issues that are emotionally powerful and ask the learner to draw on their emotional experiences. At the same time many materials have built in affective support for the learners in such circumstances. However, not all teachers are convinced that the affect can be dealt with other than face to face. But many students do not want to deal with powerful feelings in a group, they may feel safer and happier working by themselves (anyway this is certainly true of the authors of this book!). Drawing attention to the supportive nature of learning materials can be particularly useful where a teacher is suggesting that students read some open learning materials while they are on a practice placement.

### Reflection on the way a problem is framed

Framing a problem means setting a context for it and taking an approach to it. While not everyone may be familiar with the term, everyone is familiar with that feeling of success when a problem they have grappled with for weeks is solved because they have suddenly managed to think about it in a new way – that's reframing a problem (see Schön 1991, for a fuller discussion on framing in a professional context and Goffman 1972, for a more sociologically orientated discussion of framing).

In talking about tacit assumptions earlier in this chapter it was suggested that undue emphasis on the face-to-face aspect of teaching is a tacit assumption of the role. It is, in fact, also framing the role in a very particular way and giving one aspect of it ascendancy. One effect of this is to undermine other aspects of the role. When that aspect of the role stands a chance of being eclipsed in an open learning programme it is necessary to begin to think about framing teaching in a different way. In this chapter it is suggested that the frame that can usefully be adopted is not really very different from the traditional frame but is one that gives other aspects of the role more status. It is useful to think about framing teaching as *staging a performance* as well as or instead of *giving* a performance. And thus the other roles assume equal if not more importance than they did before. So that is one important way of reflecting on framing issues. However, in addition, there will also of course be issues to do with framing in the materials themselves and their delivery.

When a teacher uses open learning materials, the materials themselves will usually frame conceptual and academic problems as part of the learning package (we discuss this more fully in Chapters 4 and 5). However, they may frame the problems for a particular audience (for example the DLC's Research Awareness packs although heavily process-based and potentially of use to a wide range of health-care workers is actually framed as a nursing and midwifery pack illustrated with nursing and midwifery problems). The way that open learning materials are framed does provide a very real job of translating for the teacher. Whatever the materials used it should be possible to present learners with a number of alternative ways of framing the problem (or ask them to reframe a problem from a number of different points of view as an activity for a group session). This should help with ideas about any complementary materials that might be usefully developed: for example, a case study putting the client's point of view, or one putting the point of view of a line manager or a member of another occupation.

As we have said above, learners may see a problem framed for nursing as inappropriate to them because they are from a different occupation. For the teacher the role in communicating with them can be to help them frame the issues in the text so they see them as relevant is very much one involving the process of translation. It is helping people structure the content in a way that leads to successful learning. This is particularly important when we come to the 'isms'. Many people feel because they work in an area where, for example, there are few people from minority ethnic groups that there is no cause for them to engage with materials that are overtly anti-racist, 'this has nothing to do with us'. Similarly people working in an area where they do not encounter older people may feel that ageism has nothing to do with them when they encounter it addressed in open learning material. However, although materials may not measure up to reality as experienced by the learners, the health-care occupations are committed to taking these issues on. For example, the nursing code of practice is insistent upon the notion of service to all and people in the health-care occupations are potentially going to be using their skills with a wide spectrum of clients. The wider framing of the problem for health-care workers in a national and institutional environment becomes important. Problems need to be framed to accommodate the wider context not merely the micro-details of face-to-face encounters.

### Reflection on the role constructed by the helper for him- or herself within the larger organization

In using reflective practice as a way of constituting a role for oneself it is necessary to realize that this frequently involves reflecting about other people's roles too, notably the roles of learners and the roles of other personnel involved in an open learning scheme. A change in the teacher's role should bring about a change in theirs too. Many people are resistant to the role changes of others. They find them threatening. Learners may find having the spotlight shone on them is inconvenient and means they have to think too much. Managers may consider that the role change an open learning enthusiast wants to bring about in her work is an optional extra rather than a central and necessary change to the way that she goes about her job. There has been a real problem in some institutions in that managers and people in control have seen open learning as an optional extra that people can tackle (i.e. develop learning materials) on the top of a full-time commitment to face-to-face teaching. With the promotion of mixed-mode teaching this tendency may have died down a bit now but it certainly does a disservice to both open and traditional teaching in that teachers caught in this dilemma do not have time to fulfil either role successfully without high cost in stress to themselves.

Another institutional issue that many open learning teachers face is that of practice. Even if a teacher's involvement with her learners does not have a direct practice base it is still often the case that her learners are going to have to go out and use their knowledge in a practice situation. And this is where the roles of resource person and broker for the learners comes in very strongly. The teacher is often the person who is the interface between the knowledge and the practice. So it is a good idea for her to consider how she can help learners make connections. As a teacher she is acting within a larger organization both as an educationalist and as a member of the organization. Similarly in practice placements learners will both be learners and in some capacity members of the organization. What happens to learners in practice placements is in some respects a form of socialization. People have to 'learn' what the hierarchy is and what their place in it is. And this is something that the teacher may want to elaborate on when she has them back in class or in comments on work or telephone calls. In addition although practice may relate to some specific technical area of nursing or occupational therapy the teacher may want to spend some time in group sessions (or on the telephone or in written comments) working through how the practice placement *felt* as well as how it went. The teacher supports learners not only through direct inter-action but also by helping them use open learning materials. This is a good example of that aspect of the teacher's role we have called brokerage.

While reflection may not solve all the problems and will not auto-matically solve role discrepancies, it will certainly focus the attention and help teachers (whether committed personally or by their institution) to define the issues and problems more explicitly.

In this chapter we began by offering a number of suggestions about new roles for teachers and went on to explore some of the ways that can be used to reflect on the role. All of this might be described as preliminary work contextualizing the potential for a teacher's role in an open learn-ing context. Perhaps in thinking about reconstituting roles we should be looking to an image like a kaleidoscope where the little pieces of glass remain the same but the pattern is thoroughly reconstituted every time the kaleidoscope is turned round. We already have some little glass beads in the kaleidoscope and have a chance to shake in some new ones as the multiple role of an open learning teacher emerges.

Of course, the breakdown into all these component roles on paper may sound like wild role overload. You may be asking yourself 'How can something that no longer involves transmitting knowledge (previously a main component) actually involve so much more?' In answer to this conundrum:

- there are lots of compatibilities between some of the roles: as has been shown in Figure 3.1 – they can be mapped so as to show commonalities;
- the teacher is not 'doing' all of them all the time; one face-to-face session or telephone call might involve switching between three or four roles;
- the sorts of balances and counterbalances required to do all these sub roles are already *in situ* with the traditional teaching role and can be transferred for many aspects of the new role.

Chapters 4 and 5 go on to look in more detail at open learning materials themselves since these are the primary resources that have changed the traditional teaching role.

*Four*

# Orienting to
# materials: choosing

At the Open Learning Institute of Hong Kong we purchase materials from at least five different sources. When these embody carefully designed instruction, the Institute does not amend the material other than provide supplements of local relevance. If we must purchase material with poor design we intervene. The intervention becomes easier with the use of modern technology and erudite personnel, but still imposes an unwarranted and costly burden on the adapting institution.

(Dhanarajan and Timmers 1992: 5)

In this chapter and Chapter 5 we look at how to buy and how to adapt open learning materials. We do not intend to focus on the production of learning materials *ab initio* because we consider that large-scale materials production is best left to specialist producers.

Where good materials cannot be bought in – either because they do not exist or are too expensive – quality might be best assured by the delivery of that part of the curriculum through face-to-face teaching. If this is difficult for students, strategies such as weekend schools and summer schools might be considered. So, like the Open Learning Institute of Hong Kong, we assume that you will be concerned primarily with the identification and selection of appropriate learning materials. However, as Dhanarajan and Timmers point out, external sources of learning materials may not be totally adequate for one reason or another, and in Chapter 5, we look more closely at some of the more useful aspects of 'home' production, particularly adaptation and development. However, this chapter explores the process of 'buying in' materials from external producers. As with any purchase the old maxim 'Let the buyer beware' is the foundation of good practice. While many producers are publicly funded HEIs, it would be a mistake not to see that they are in business to sell products. You are unlikely to find producers writing to you to say that they think their product is unsuited to your needs. So, as the buyer, you need a clear idea of what learning materials *can* do – what the parameters of quality are – as well as what *you* want them to do.

## What can open learning materials do?

Open learning materials have to do what a good teacher would do: stimulate interest and enquiry, provide appropriate examples, explain new ideas, ask questions, and so on. Many teachers, particularly experienced ones, handle a good many of these kinds of interactions with their students almost intuitively. Once they are 'performing' they use the tools of their trade, their favourite anecdotes, resources and exercises, to elicit responses from their students. They are in turn sparked off by students' answers and comments and a rich dialogue may develop. It may only be when there is the challenge of planning some teaching on a completely new topic or during the rigour of a validation process that teachers stop and think carefully in detail about the sequence of inputs and the range of possible teaching devices that are effective for learners. And then looking back at specific sessions and courses they will probably be able to point to aspects of the course that went really well. Key words are those like 'It never fails', 'It always gets them going', 'I don't do that any more because they don't respond to it'. Such evaluations, of course, emerge because a teacher has been there on the spot, able to gauge reactions, able to adjust her own performance and so on.

In contrast, consider the situation materials developers find themselves in. Careful pre-planning must be the norm: the dialogue with learners has to be predicted and built into the materials well before the learning programme is delivered. Materials developers cannot think on their feet and decide to substitute a different activity because it builds on a discussion the learners are currently having. With learning materials, everything the teacher might want to say to learners has to be thought of in advance, and their responses have to be anticipated. It is one half of a conversation where the teacher does not always know how people will reply but nevertheless needs to keep the interaction going. At the same time, the individual students working with the materials should feel that the words and exercises are fresh and presented specially to help their learning. Rowntree (1992a) has coined the term 'tutorial in print' to stress the interactive nature of open learning materials.

As successful face-to-face teaching performances are often rather intuitive but the producers of open learning materials need to be highly systematic, there is great value to the purchaser in reviewing an analysis of the learning process of the sort provided by Gagné. In *The Conditions of Learning* (1965), Gagné considers systematically the sequence of inputs needed for an effective learning process. The following list is based on Gagné's sequence of key conditions:

1 Gain the learner's attention and engage their interest.
2 Spell out the expected learning outcomes.
3 Remind the learner of relevant earlier learning and experience.
4 Present new information or experience.
5 Guide learner to undertake learning activities.
6 Provide speedy feedback on activities.
7 Provide opportunities to apply learning to other situations.
8 Help learner to see generalizability of the newly acquired capability.
9 Guide learner to practice and use the new capability.
10 Provide for learner's performance to be verified.

It can be seen that this sequence fits satisfactorily with the sort of interaction successful face-to-face teachers engage in with learners. However, with regard to learning materials some of the stages in the list are easier than others to achieve. Presenting new information has often been handled through print or other media, sometimes to the extent where 'book learning' has dominated to the exclusion of learning from experience. Feedback and performance appraisal are harder to handle through materials alone and it might be necessary to bring in a teacher's input – but the materials will still need to orchestrate this.

Gagné was dealing with simpler learning outcomes than we are often concerned with. Nevertheless, even highly complex pieces of learning can be broken down into a series of somewhat simpler learning chunks that, with suitable guidance, will accumulate and contribute to the overall learning outcome. Learning materials therefore need a definite structure. At the development stage, structure helps authors, in the absence of student feedback, to ensure that they are not leaving gaps and, at the delivery stage, helps students to feel secure in the absence of a teacher. Structured learning materials are particularly helpful for establishing a clear framework for students, in which they can see clear short-term goals, well-defined tasks and an overall sense of purpose in their studies. A high level of structure in open learning materials may be particularly valuable for part-time and in-service students who need to fit the discipline of studying into an already busy life. Such materials can also be more helpful than might be thought in establishing study patterns with new students. The sort of structure that can be derived for Gagné's 'conditions of learning' translates into the following features and typical pattern of open learning materials.

| *Item* | *Function* |
| --- | --- |
| 1 Introduction | Explains what is to come and where the learning is heading |
| 2 Orienting question/quiz | Gets learner's interest/stimulates recall of relevant information/experience |
| 3 Feedback | Gives typical replies and uses these to raise series of key questions |
| 4 Text 1 | Provides new content |
| 5 Self-assessment question 1 | Enables learners to check their response to the text |
| 6 Text: Case study | Applies new content to real life |
| 7 Activity and checklist | Helps learners to apply learning to their own situation |
| 8 Text 2 | Provides further content |
| 9 Self-assessment question 2 | Enables learners to check their understanding of links between content |
| 10 Discussion of self-assessment question 2 | Enables learners to assess how adequate their responses are |
| 11 Text: example | Applies content to real-life example |
| 12 Cumulative test on text 1 and text 2 | Enables learners to check mastery of learning objectives |
| 13 Summary checklist | Summarizes teaching points and acts as guide to future action |

This kind of structure can be found in many effective learning materials. The key things to notice are:

- the repeating *tell–teach–test* sequence, which is the basic building block for learning materials;
- frequent *activities and questions* of different kinds;
- regular opportunities for learners to check and *verify their learning*;
- the use of *introduction* and *summary* to top and tail the sequence, making it a stand-alone chunk of learning.

A different structure, also noted by Rowntree (1992a), is based on the notion of reflection. Guided by this philosophy, materials may be more concerned with directing the learner outward towards a range of learning experiences or inwards to explore memories of practice and critical incidents. The idea of reflection has been well rehearsed within health-care literature (see, for example, Benner 1984 and Johns 1994) but it has also been a primary theme in recent literature on open learning (see, for example, Evans and Nation 1993 and Harris 1987). Here we would want to propose that the 'tutorial in print' approach and the 'reflective' approach are on a continuum. There is no basic contradiction between them and many materials may usefully contain both approaches. There are implications for materials developers, as to where they are on the continuum. For example, writing a learning programme with a high level of affect is significant in terms of how feedback is constructed. And 'test' becomes a very different concept depending on whether you are talking about changing a bed or changing an attitude. But certainly, as far as programmes related to practice are concerned, materials often need to include both a critique of what goes on and how it feels. Clearly a student would dismiss material that attempted to feedback a 'right' answer about feelings as crass, but in contrast would expect to receive substantive feedback to a technical question. But in between these two extremes there are a variety of possibilities for helpful feedback to learners, some of which may well be tell–teach–test and others primarily reflective.

The problem for purchasers is that few producers of materials are explicit about their educational approach. Purchasers need to get involved with the materials – perhaps ask potential learners to test them – to see what the integral approaches are. You will find two examples of learning materials that show fundamentally different learning approaches at the end of the chapter (Examples 1 and 2). The first is by and large a tutorial in print, the second offers a more reflective approach. Each, however, occasionally edges along towards the other end of the continuum. Interestingly, although each was produced by a different course team in a different faculty, both were produced by the OU for their students. The first, however, is intended primarily for undergraduates, the second for professional and lay workers in health care.

A potential purchaser of open learning materials will be interested in both:

- the content of the material;
- how the learner is engaged and encouraged to learn.

In order to analyse the features of structured learning further the following sections look at both these areas in some detail.

## Content features of open learning materials

The content of any course is going to be presented in a specific way (or ways). It may be presented as a progressing argument; as a combination of descriptions and analyses; as experiments and conclusions; as charts and analyses; as juxtaposed examples followed by comparisons. So it can be seen that as well as containing facts or described experiences, the content will be structured so that comparisons, analyses, syntheses, refutations and conclusions put forward 'positions' on the content. In addition, the choice of content will, by definition, mean that other potential content is left out. In other words, the authors will have presented a particular picture of the subject area. To use an artistic analogy, this might be like a collage with lots of views put together, or it might be a distinctive approach to the subject like impressionism. Exploring how the content is presented will be part of the evaluative process any potential purchaser of learning materials will want to go through. The choices to be made will relate to curriculum constraints, occupational aims and academic judgement. To continue the artistic analogy, an impressionistic painting will not do if what you really want is an 'old master'.

In this chapter we merely want to alert you to the importance of unearthing what the angle on the materials is and checking if it fits with your needs. In Chapter 5 we go on to explore issues around what happens when the fit between the materials and what you want is not adequate. Issues we would highlight when looking for fit include the way in which both practitioners and clients are portrayed. Anecdotal evidence suggests that purchasers of (otherwise useful) learning materials experience a great deal of difficulty with their students when the materials do not accurately convey the reality of the lives of learners or their clients. This reality may be conveyed through text – *his* or *her* used exclusively without explanation, for example – but most often problems arise with visual images that sharply convey a reality that may be alien to the learner. This issue may be connected with the gross structures of equal opportunities – black/white, female/male – but may also be related to subtle images of inclusion/exclusion, recognition/non-recognition. If the intricate detail of the learner's life is not compatible with that portrayed in the materials, then the learning cannot connect with and embrace the reality of the learner.

This issue is especially relevant in health-care education in relation to the portrayal of practice reality and may be familiar to those using learning materials with experienced practitioners. If the learners feel that the practice portrayed is idealized or inadequate then they will simply disconnect themselves and their learning from it and therefore the value of the materials is lessened. An example of such materials that we have used is the videotape in P553 *A Systematic Approach to Nursing Care*. This shows a sequence of nursing activities designed to portray assessment, evaluation, and so on but few of the recorded sequences manage to convey the complexity and difficulty of practice. Audiences often just find it funny and the original intentions of offering a 'role model' have been abandoned in favour of using the materials as simply a basis for discussion. This is an interesting example of how material that may not fulfil its original purpose can still be turned to another use through a flexible approach by the teacher.

More concretely, the authors can assert their experience of this phenomenon as producers. When producing materials for nurses, there is strong pressure from members of the nursing profession to upgrade the 'academic' nature of the learning materials – that is, to assert that nursing 'really is' highly academic. Politically this may be an important message that they want the materials to carry. The problem is that many, perhaps most, nurses experience difficulty understanding and connecting with highly academic materials. This tension between talking to the learner in their own language or experience and using the desired language of academic credibility may be found in many learning materials and it may be useful, if properly handled, in introducing practitioners to one of the tensions inherent in their profession.

## Flexibility

We have already noted that one of the benefits of open learning materials is that learners can take them into the practice setting. In choosing materials it is useful to consider how linear the curriculum is. For example, if Module 7 is the module most pertinent to practice, are students going to be able to make some sense of it even if they have not yet fully grasped Modules 1–6? Are the materials structured so that the student is able to 'drop in' to various small sections that might be particularly attractive in a practice setting? Or is it absolutely necessary that modules 1–6 are completely assimilated before Module 7 can be tackled? Practice situations have a habit of throwing up all sorts of conceptual, affective and practice problems that do not unfold as neatly as an open learning package (or a face-to-face taught course, for that matter). It is therefore advantageous if students feel able to refer to a number of parts of a course during their practice placements. You can test out the flexibility of materials by considering some of the issues that have in the past arisen for your students and then critically examining the open learning package you are considering buying with these in mind. Which topics/ sections would be relevant? How easy is it to read them as free-standing units?

## Theory and practice

Practice often does not 'present' as theory. Real life is usually a good deal messier than theory. How is theory dealt with in the courses you are examining? For many people involved in practice education, theory is a means to an end. It is not the 'leading edge'; it is a way of making sense of real situations with which people are confronted. How easy will it be for your students to 'apply' the theories in a specific package? Clearly this is an issue that a course team should discuss as it develops notions of curriculum. There may well be a shopping list of the sorts of theories that need to be dealt with. But should they be dealt with as theory *per se*, or should they be embedded in real-life examples? Some learning packages can do this latter work. They may begin with the experience and lives of practitioners and service users, which is analysed theoretically. This is not to say such texts are superior for all purposes but to suggest that if a curriculum is going to place value on your students' experience then the materials chosen will be better suited to your curriculum if they begin with real lives, real experience and real practice.

### Learner management and support features

There are other structures that can be seen to exist in open learning materials. While the content structure to some extent demonstrates the authors' position, the learning structures and presentation features should encapsulate a template of what the learner is like and what the learner needs. There are two important questions to be asked here by teachers. First, how do materials manage the path of the learner through the learning process; what mechanisms or techniques will act on the learner to achieve the desired ends? Second, what ends are we trying to achieve? Where do we want the learner to go; what do we want her to do? The first question is rather easier to answer than the second and this section will describe and give examples of a range of 'devices' to guide the learner. At various times we will allude to the way in which devices can support different educational philosophies, but the degree to which any particular educational philosophy is apparent in the selection and use of devices in learning materials is a subjective interpretation.

We will talk about devices with reference to the following purposes:

- generating *access;*
- generating *motivation.*

### Access

Everyone is familiar with the uncomfortable feelings generated by being in a strange place and not knowing the rules of behaviour. But sometimes we forget that new students may feel like strangers as they try to negotiate the corridors of educational buildings and have to enter rooms full of unknown people. The student 'entering' a package of open learning materials may feel just the same, although she may at least be in the comfort of her own home and beyond the critical gaze of others. But materials can be structured in ways that make the student feel comfortable and safe just as student induction processes can make people feel welcome.

Generating accessibility is an important part of this process that not only draws the student into the material but allows them to stop and recommence their study without difficulties or barriers. Hodgson (1993) lists a number of devices which enhance student access to materials:

- contents list;
- summaries;
- index;
- glossary;
- headings;
- cross-referencing;
- advance organisers;
- pre-tests;
- concept structure diagrams;
- lists of aims and objectives;
- presentation.

Many of these are familiar to teachers from their work with books; below we discuss several that are particularly important in open learning materials.

### Advance organizers

Obviously, sections marked *Introduction* will help learners to understand what to expect in the following materials. For example, the Introduction sections from the DLC Research Awareness series at the end of the chapter (Example 3) illustrates what the section can do. It starts by describing the whole Research Awareness series and the overall aims. It goes on to talk about self-directed learning and describes the devices that the learners will find in the text, including activities, commentary, further reading, references, offprints and progress boxes. The process of developmental testing is then described – a benefit for the purchasers as well as the learners. The final section in the Introduction tries to help the student anticipate and deal with the process of studying.

So, advance organizers can tell the learners where they are going and what it might be like when they get there. In some texts, however, advance organizers can get out of hand and learners may feel that they are forever following the signposts and never reaching the destination. A good text strikes a balance, alerting the learner to the structure of the course but not bogging them down in it.

*Aims and objectives*

The question of whether courses and learners should orient to aims and objectives is a difficult one and relates to the structure versus reflection debate. But in general terms it is important that students know why they are studying and what they can reasonably expect to gain from this particular text. This may be particularly important where students need to achieve specific knowledge or competencies before they are safe to practice.

Learning materials may include a very specific list of aims and/or objectives at the beginning of each section. An alternative approach, which is characteristic of much of the material produced by the DLC, is to describe what the student should expect to know *after* the section in which they studied it. Examples of each approach are shown at the end of the chapter (Examples 4 and 5).

Sometimes, lists of objectives are referenced and reinforced by specific questions, as in Example 6 from *Dilemmas in Health Care*: The rationale for this latter approach is that it can be quite intimidating for learners to be presented with a list of what they will learn before they start. Placed at the end, a list of aims and objectives has more of a feedback function: it alerts the learners to issues they might have missed and may help to summarize the preceding text. Either way, clear indication of what the learning process is aiming towards offers students the ability to choose how much time to devote to it, and the possibility of reflecting on whether they have reached the specified goal.

*Headings*

Headings also serve as 'signposts' to help students know what particular sections are about and to choose whether or not to access them. Cross-headings label the passage that follows them. Sometimes there are also side headings in the margins to indicate key passages. Running headings, either at the top or bottom (in which case they are known as footings) of the page, also help the student find passages that they want to access or return to. One of the things that good open learning materials should do is 'grammaticize' the learning. That is to say, just as sentences are assisted by subclauses, parentheses and emphases, so open learning should be printed in a format that learners come to recognize as coherent and structured. Headings of several sizes and formats can help this process as long as they are used consistently.

*Presentation*

All the aspects of the way in which materials are presented can increase or decrease the access potential. The area of typographic structure is a complex and interesting one, and to a certain extent the choices made by authors and by the graphic artists are subjective ones. However, pages can be laid out in a user friendly way by choosing a reasonable print size (usually 10 or 11 point) and by including lots of white space on each page. Different types of content can be indicated through the use of different fonts, boxes, lines, bullet points, etc. and this all helps the student know what sort of activity is required of them at that point. This is a further reflection of the notion of a sensible grammar for an open learning text: something which looks good, reads well and imposes a recognizable order consistent throughout the materials.

However, there is a tendency in some open learning text to 'over-egg the pudding', which results in a page of text so busy that it becomes difficult to read. Clearly one aim is to avoid pages of didactic text during which nothing much is demanded of the reader but passive reading: but a text in which the reader never knows what will happen next and cannot settle to any systematic style of work may be irritating and disturbing. For a critical reader assessing open learning materials it is important to note those moments when she is not sure what she is supposed to read next. It is usually a good sign of a poorly presented text and yet it is something frequently ignored by competent readers who implicitly assume they are not concentrating hard enough if they do not know what to do next.

The question of how a text is bound may not seem very important but those with experience of being an open learning student often remember the binding of the text as a major threat to ease of study. Moya Davis, who has been at various times an open learning student, tutor and author, talks about the need for each student to have four baked bean tins – one to hold down each corner of the text! Other people may recall the annoyance of a single printed sheet coming away in one's hands as pages are turned (and no matter how much care is taken, once the pages start to escape it is a hopeless case!). Texts that are spiral bound are easier to use than so-called perfect binding that often refuses to lie flat. But spiral binding is, of course, expensive.

### Design

Like any other consumer object, the aesthetic design of open learning materials can add considerably to the pleasure of their use, and therefore increase the learner's motivation. If a text is pleasant to look at and to handle then the learner will want to get it out from the cupboard and work with it. However, it is not simply a case of 'the glossier, the better'. Good design must also be about ease of use, and something that is good to look at may not be easy to work with. A central question when choosing text is 'Do I want the learner to write on the page?' The argument in favour is that by adding to the text the learner customizes and increases a sense of worth and ownership (more practically, it probably also means that notes and comments will not be lost). However, we have all been taught from our earliest days *not* to write on books, and a glossy design may inhibit many learners from this customizing process, and it is also quite hard to write on very glossy pages. However, you may also have to face the question of whether the materials will be re-used, in which case anything that helps prevent the learner writing on the text is helpful.

## Motivation

Once the learner has accessed the text and knows how to use it, the problem is to keep them motivated and to keep them moving through the material. A text that promotes and rewards active learning is the best motivator and we look at how that can be achieved in the next section. However, there are a number of straightforward devices that help. These include appropriate pacing, sequencing and readability, and in addition, video and audiotape components can help to change the pace of a course.

## Readability

A number of methods of checking readability of texts have been developed (notably Fog and Flesch) and some computer programs can now run a readability check on text in production. It is possible, therefore, that authors will have tried to develop text to certain levels of readability and aimed, say, at the level of reading required for a daily tabloid newspaper or for a broadsheet newspaper. Unfortunately, very few open learning programmes publicize the levels of reading they have written to, and in any case the subject is quite controversial: not all those working on texts are convinced of the efficacy of readability checks. However, any critical reader may like to reflect on the sort of level of reading a package is written in. Does it read like a popular magazine, a broadsheet or tabloid, or is it like a piece of legal writing? Each of these styles has a particular function and an audience that will easily cope with the style, and it is really up to the critical reader to consider the extent to which the style of writing might be attractive to various learner groups.

## Illustrations

A further issue that can be contentious is the use of illustration. Hodgson (1993) lists a number of things that illustrations can do in an open learning text:

- description – to show what something looks like when words are not enough in themselves (e.g. a spiral staircase);

- explanation – to show how a complex system works and how its parts interrelate (e.g. a central heating system);
- demonstration – to demonstrate a particular task to be carried out (e.g. dressing wounds);
- expression – to elicit an emotional response in the learners (e.g. Charitable Aid 'type' pictures of malnutrition);
- motivation – to 'lighten' and add variety to a dense and/or long text (e.g. cartoons);
- memorization – to make an abstract concept more memorable by associating it with visual imagery (e.g. Newton's apple).

It has to be said that for many open learning materials developers, illustrations often end up by being fillers. But text that does use illustration creatively adds an extra dimension to the print.

### Audio and video

Not all open learning packages contain audio or video components. Video, in particular, is expensive to produce (even for large institutions dedicated to open learning). However, both can be extremely useful for changing pace for the learner engaged in the course. Listening to real people talking about their experience can be very involving for learners (and adds to the dialogue in the package). In addition to experiential discussion, audiotapes can be particularly useful for taking learners through a difficult diagram or exploring, say, responses to practice. It will be noticed that while a diagram could be a way of translating a difficult piece of text (see above) it could also be explained on audio, thus giving the learners a number of 'goes' at one particularly difficult concept. Those learners who grasp it easily can be advised not to use more than one medium or will themselves decide that they have 'got it' after one explanation.

### Active learning features

One of the central tenets of open learning materials is that active learning features are one of the main motivating features for learners. Of course, active learning can take place in all parts of open learning materials, but these are particular devices the function of which is to draw the learner further into the learning process. There are a variety of activities the student is asked to undertake that are sometimes defined in different ways such as:

- activities;
- exercises;
- self-assessment questions (SAQs);
- in-text questions (ITQs).

Activities can ask the learner to do any number of things – reflect on their own experience, use a given data set to work something out, provide data to feed into a model, reflect on previous information derived from examples in the materials, rank or prioritize criteria and so on. Whatever the task, the emphasis is on action by the student. However, in order for activities to get done they also need to be either enjoyable to undertake or essential to progression. Enjoyment may come from the nature of the activity itself or from the feedback on success that the student receives. Whether or not any activity is essential depends on the degree to which it is integrated into the rest of the learning material, and this may in turn depend on how the materials were written. Learning materials may be written in a fairly didactic mode, and the activities added at the end to highlight key learning points. Alternatively, the activities may all be written first and the supporting text then feeds into the activities. It is simple to tell the difference between these modes – in the first mode the text makes sense without the activities, in the second it does not. If the text can be read without any reference to the activities then the temptation for the learner to skip them is very strong. However, while this may recommend the second mode to you as purchaser, it should be remembered that many learners like to read the whole text to get an overview and then return to the beginning and start to study slowly including the activities as they go along – in this case, text that does not make any sense until the activities are completed may be irritating to the learner. Furthermore, text in which all the activities *must* be completed gives the learner little leeway for choice. One way to get around this problem is to choose a text that is at neither of the extreme ends of the spectrum, and use other devices to increase the learner's desire to complete the activities. The most obvious one is to base group activities on feedback from individual activities, and we shall say more about this in Chapter 6. Assessment can also be linked to the activities. In some assessed courses learners may feel under so much pressure that they will inevitably not do some activities, focusing only on those they consider to be germane to the assessment. We have included three examples from very different learning texts to show a range of styles and devices available to authors at the end of the chapter (Examples 7, 8 and 9). Clearly the degree of involvement required from the learner in each example is very different.

## Resource considerations

Chapter 2 introduced the issue of costing briefly, but even in this more detailed section we cannot consider the cost of open learning materials in the abstract because there are too many context specific variables to consider. In any case, the basic question should be not, 'what do they cost?', but, 'what are they worth?'. Education is often considered to be a cost rather than an investment, and never more so than when the costs of learning materials are printed at the bottom of an invoice. However, leaving those considerations aside, it is important to consider costs. First, there is the question of what costs are dictated by the learning materials; second, the question of what hidden costs the use of these materials might incur and to whom.

### Prescribed costs

While many learning materials suggest a range of complementary activities, some prescribe a range of activities that are essential to the learning experience. An obvious example is a course such as P554 *Child Abuse and Neglect*, produced by the Open University. Because of the sensitive nature of the subject, the Course Team took the view that group work would be an essential part of the learning experience. The Groupwork Guide is therefore an extensive and important part of the learning materials and the course cannot be completed without attendance at the group sessions. Thus this decision shapes the cost of the package. But it is at least explicit, the purchaser is aware of it and it derives from a serious concern for the learner that you as a purchaser can accept (and buy) or reject (and decide not to buy).

### Hidden costs

However, not all 'costs' are so up front. Consider the following example of an open learning activity:

> Go to the library and read up on other kinds of psychological interventions which could help patients with skin problems.
>
> (RCN 1994b: 6)

Clearly this assumes that learners have access to a library with appropriate resources. But the following question arises: 'how many learners might want the information at the same time?' If there was insufficient information on the shelves, students might then want to search for more, using electronic searching systems and extra librarian time, with the resulting costs to the institution.

An alternative approach to resourcing, which is largely based on OU practice, is to include all necessary materials in the pack, usually in a Reader or 'Offprint' section, as in this example:

> Read the article by Caroline Flint entitled 'Fact-finding mission' (Offprint 10). By discussing examples from midwifery, this short

paper illustrates the importance of questioning nursing practice and identifies the many opportunities available for you to do so.

(DLC 1987b: 5)

There is obviously a 'trade off' here between the two approaches we have just cited. For the purchasers the first approach will reduce the cost of materials but may increase the costs to other budgets, such as the library. There are educational differences too; the second approach offers an easier studying route and may help those working difficult hours and those isolated from a library: whereas the first might encourage use of a library and reinforce literature searching skills.

A slightly different resource issue is illustrated by these activities:

1 I would like you to establish some system of recording nursing questions and problems in your place of work. You might like to consider using a box, a file, a notebook, or some other method that is suitable for your own particular situation.
2 Now try the system out by recording all the questions that you have asked in the earlier activities of this module.
3 Once you have established your system, I want you to introduce it to colleagues working alongside you, and encourage them to ask questions and record their ideas.

(DLC 1987b: 20)

Choose one case study opposite, discuss it with colleagues and then:

1 Identify the local problems at the wound site.
2 Complete the wound assessment.
3 List any other factors that you would wish to assess for this patient.
4 List the principal options for local wound management (see references under Further Reading for principles of dressing selection and the manufacturers' latest product data sheets).
5 List the advantages and disadvantages of each.
6 Draw up a care plan for the patient including the management of more general factors, indicated in the case study, that could delay healing.
7 List any self-help advice or practical instructions that you would give the patient and his/her carers.
8 State how and when you would evaluate the effectiveness of the care you propose to give.
9 Outline a long-term plan for the patient's care, including planned patient education and any follow-up care that might be required in the community, where the scenario begins in hospital.

(RCN 1994a: 8)

In the example from the DLC's Research Awareness Module 5, the first two parts of the activity could be completed by the learner acting alone – using only her own resources. The third part of the activity requires an additional input of resource from her colleagues. Similarly in the second example, part of the activity involves discussion with colleagues, although it is less obviously an integral part of the activity. If input from colleagues or others is an absolute requirement for the successful completion of the activity that may need detailed costing or may, especially if the learner is unsupported by her employers, be difficult to arrange. However, it may have enormous benefits in improving practice. One of the great assets of learning materials is that they have a physical presence and can often be shared with colleagues. The discussion of the work of an activity may lead to enquiry about the preceding text and generate an exciting and productive debate about change in practice.

Concern over the costs of learners' activities is not unique to open learning. However, for two reasons it is particularly problematic. The first is that producers of learning materials are isolated from the realities of the costs. To suggest that students 'request information from the Community Health Council (CHC)', for example, may seem like a good idea to a producer who does not know that any CHC adjacent to a university is likely to find that 25 per cent of enquiries come from learners on University courses. The second reason is that supporters of the 'reflective practice' mode of open learning may encourage students to engage with external agencies without specific regard for the costs involved. Without wishing to characterize either school, it is probably fair to suggest that proponents of highly structured learning are most keen to include all necessary resources in the learning package. Those who consider that this is unnecessarily restrictive may need to consider the costs of relatively unstructured learning to other agencies.

### Costs to learners

A further aspect of 'hidden' costs is that, within an open learning programme, some costs may be transferred to the learner. The stereotypical open learning student studying in the back bedroom while the family sleeps is incurring costs – heating, lighting, extra coffee! She (or her employers) may well be saving some travel costs, and the equation for each learner is unique, but nevertheless, it is reasonable to characterize open learning as 'privatizing' learning and to consider the redistribution of costs.

## The process of selection

We have offered a number of features of open learning materials that you may wish to explore in examining packages. Undoubtedly the best way to act upon such listings is to review plenty of materials. Looking at a couple of packages in detail probably will not be sufficient to 'get your eye in'. The best way to get to grips with it all is to scan a lot of material, including materials not particularly relevant to your subject area. Competitive judgements become easier as you get a feel for the types of activities, the number of examples, the use of headings and so on.

However, while it is important that buyers have a good grasp of the nature of materials it is unrealistic to suppose that they can work through many sets of materials in great detail. A useful approach is to develop a checklist that will serve to begin the process of choosing. Rowntree's (1992a) checklist is shown as Example 10 at the end of the chapter.

Amendments to this checklist can be developed to suit particular needs, particularly with reference to local needs, circumstances and preferences.

EXAMPLE 1

# 8 Health care in the Third World, 1974 to the 1990s

*This chapter builds upon your knowledge and understanding of health and disease in Third World countries, based on the study of* World Health and Disease. *In particular, we suggest that you refresh your memory of the diversity of health experience between and within Third World countries by referring back to Chapters 2 and 8 of that book, and revising the complex connections between economic development, population growth and social inequality.*

*During your study of the present chapter, you will be asked to read an article in the Reader by David Werner, 'The village health worker: lackey or liberator?'. A television programme about health care in Zimbabwe relates directly to this chapter, but an earlier television programme and audiotape—both entitled 'Health and Disease in Zimbabwe'—are also relevant.*

## Introduction

This chapter continues the discussion of contemporary diversity in health care by providing a broad overview of health and health-care systems in the Third World and the way in which health policies have changed. It covers the period from the 1970s to the 1990s and focuses on a revolutionary change in health policy—*the primary health care movement.* The main questions addressed are:

- Why was there such a significant change in Third World health policy? What led to the introduction of the primary health care approach?

- How was primary health care interpreted when ministries of health in Third World countries tried to put policy into practice?

- What have been the main problems in the implemention of primary health care in the Third World?

Although the primary health care movement was by no means limited to the Third World (its counterpart in the industrialised world, as you have seen in Chapter 7, was in health-centre expansion, primary health care teams, health promotion, and the new public health), this chapter focuses on developing countries.

### The many faces of the Third World

Although it is useful to use the term 'Third World' as shorthand, it is important to remind you that it represents a heterogeneous grouping of nations, not a bloc in terms of income and wealth.

□ Summarise some of the main dimensions of diversity within and between Third World countries.[1]

■ You might have thought of some of the following categories (to which we have added examples in brackets):

1  *GNP per capita* (ranges from 120 US$ in Ethiopia to 2 970 US$ in Gabon).

2  *Under-five mortality rates* (226 per 1 000 population in that age-group in Ethiopia, 167 per 1 000 in Gabon).

3  *Population size* (Nigeria has a population of over 100 million; Botswana, which is almost the same geographical area, has just over 1 million people).

[1] As discussed in *World Health and Disease*, Chapters 2, 3 and 8.

4   *Rural–urban differentials* (infant mortality rates in Mozambique's capital, Maputo, are about 90 per 1 000 live births but in some rural areas are 173 per 1 000 live births).

5   *Intra-urban differentials* (in Manila the infant mortality rate in the urban slums is three times higher than in other parts of the city).

Infant and under-five mortality rates declined in the first decades after World War II, and continued decreasing into the 1970s. Since the mid-1980s, however, the position is not clear in the poorest countries. Economic stagnation and recession have led to deteriorating health conditions, and in some countries it is feared that there will be a significant increase in child mortality in the 1990s.

Consequently, when we look at indicators of health in the Third World we look at a world of huge contrasts. And those differences are reflected in many other ways. A worker in Benin described two faces of Africa, but he could just as well have been writing about Asia or Latin America:

> There is the educated, literate, charming and welcoming Africa where the tourists go, where the business people trade and where project coordinators hatch their schemes. There the five star hotels, exotic cuisine, swimming pools and safari clubs with telexes, telephones and faxes. There the ministries of health or development, there the besuited people with power and influence. But there is the second Africa, usually beyond the city boundaries, beyond the tarmac and neon lights, perhaps 50 km away along dusty or muddy tracks where there are no banks or telephones and children are taught in crumbling mud brick shelters that pass for schools. There where English or French is hardly spoken, where the locals babble away in tongues unknown to Western ears, where clothing is faded and torn, where grins are so often toothless. There where chickens and goats scratch for food around the family cooking pot and naked babies play in the dirt. (Potter, 1991, p. 1 558)

Differences between rural and urban populations persist. But it is *urbanisation* that has increased over the past decades, and which demands attention because of the huge inequalities between groups within cities. For many urban dwellers in slum areas, environmental conditions are damaging to health—housing overcrowded, roads and thoroughways squalid, sanitation and water supply inadequate. Access to the existing health services, medicines, doctors and nurses may be limited. Not only do poor urban dwellers have to cope with violence and injury in cities (both major causes of death), but they also suffer from infectious diseases and malnutrition as well as the chronic cardiovascular diseases and cancers typical of modern Western societies.

Data from many countries suggest a single explanation: access to the conditions that improve people's health are highly inequitable. Both rural and poor urban populations lack sufficient and clean water supplies and sanitation. Education, although widespread, is seldom available beyond primary school, and its quality is variable; employment opportunities are few, especially in rural areas. Shortage of food adds to people's vulnerability. In urban areas violence and overcrowding are threats to health. And health care is patchy: in both city and countryside, people continue to turn to practitioners of traditional or folk medicine for help when ill, sometimes because formal 'Western' care is not easily available, sometimes because they prefer, or have more confidence in, the traditional sector.

## The evolution of Third World health policy, 1970–8

Although there had been many reports about developing comprehensive health services based on health centres during and after World War II, what was actually implemented during the following decades were *centres of excellence* in many Third World countries: the university hospitals emulating the teaching hospitals of the industrialised world. As you will recall from Chapter 6, these were all in urban areas, usually in the capital, and absorbed a high percentage of the health budget. By the late 1960s, however, a real shift in thinking about medicine was occurring, although it was only in the 1970s that widespread dissemination of new ideas occurred.

Four areas of influence and changing ideas that laid the basis for primary health care, particularly in the Third World, are discernible in this period, although any such division is to some extent arbitrary and overlapping. Policy change occurs as the result of a complex series of events and ideas not easily distinguishable over time. However, it is possible to focus on four areas:

*   experiments in particular countries to find alternative means for improving health;

*   changing ideas about poverty, health and development;

*   concern about population growth;

*Source*: Webster, C. (ed.) (1993) *Caring for Health: History and Diversity*, Revised Edition, Buckingham, Open University Press, pp. 150–1.

EXAMPLE 2

# 8   *Continuity and change*

*You will need Audio Cassette 4 and the Extract Book for your work in this section.*

This section invites you to look at the link between learning and change, and at the balance between continuity and change in your life as it might affect your involvement in health and welfare. You will look at both your own and the course team's expectations of your learning and change, and the kinds of changes sometimes expected of users and service providers. We introduce our final case study material on HIV (Human Immunodeficiency Virus) infection and Aids (Acquired immune deficiency syndrome). A diagnosis of either means major changes for those affected. But the emergence of Aids has also stimulated changes in thinking and in practice. There have already been changes in roles and relationships, at a personal level and between service users and providers.

## 8.1   Learning and change

As you reach the end of this course, you will have a good idea of the expectations the course team had of you. In particular, you will have your own ideas about the quality of the course material, the range of different types of learning material, and its complexity. The impact we expected the course to have on you might be less clear. Has it radically changed your life? Do you look upon others involved in the health and welfare field with a significantly different understanding?

Change can be subtle, and it is not always easy to recognise how much you have changed. It may not be until much later that you realise how much change has taken place. Not all change is for the better, and to attribute all changes that may have occurred in your learning to the work undertaken on a course is to underestimate the knowledge and skill that you already possessed. Jill Reynolds once congratulated a student on successfully completing a social work course after having to repeat a year of study. 'You've changed a lot', she said. The student replied, 'Actually I didn't think I needed to change that much, I thought I was pretty much OK to start with'.

Implicit in our assumptions about the course is that students will want to use what they've learnt and find some practical application for it. It is as if the course mission is to try and improve the world through the influence it has on you. Is this assumption correct in your case? Has your motivation changed as you have progressed?

**Activity** _____

**Your reasons for taking this course**

Spend just a few minutes reflecting on your responses to this activity.

Why did you take this course in the first place? Looking back, have you discovered other reasons which you weren't aware of at the time? Have your reasons for taking the course changed in any way? We have put some possible reasons below for you to consider. You may recall other reasons too:

- curiosity;
- to prove that I could do some sustained learning;
- to learn more about health and welfare services in the UK;
- to help me do my job better;
- to get promotion or a better job;
- to get an OU credit;
- to make better use of health and welfare services;
- to complete my study for the Diploma in Health and Social Welfare.

*Comment*

Clearly this course does offer a route towards a qualification. If this was the initial attraction, other expectations and consequences may have become more central to your motivation as you have undertaken the course.

Some research conducted with a range of populations in different countries explored people's motivation for undertaking learning projects (Tough, 1978). The most common motivation was the anticipated use or application of knowledge and skill. Less common was curiosity or a wish to possess the knowledge for its own sake. In this research it seemed that taking courses solely to gain credit or qualification was rare. However, qualification is often what provides an individual with the licence to make use of knowledge and skills. ◻

Alan Tough defines a learning project as:

*a highly deliberate effort to gain or retain certain definite knowledge and skill, or to change in some other way.*

*(Tough, 1978, p.250)*

This definition suggests that learning and change are closely linked. Tough found that many learning projects happen outside any official learning institutions. His broad definition allowed him to include a wide range of projects in his research. In a further study of change and learning, Tough (1982) found that most people, by their own assessment, had achieved quite a significant change through a learning project over a period of two years. However, they needed a lot of prompting to acknowledge the success of their changes:

*They are simply not in touch with the variety, competence and success of their changes, nor with how thoughtful, active and responsible they are in these changes.*

(Tough, 1982, p.77)

They lacked confidence in their own ability to see what they needed, decide for themselves what they should do about it, and work out how effective they had been. It was as if they needed someone else to tell them that they had actually learnt something and had achieved what they wanted as a result. Are you in touch with the variety, competence and success of your learning on this course? Do you feel you have been thoughtful, active and responsible in reflecting on the changes your learning has brought about in you, or might bring about in the future? Other than through the mark and comments you get for your assessed work, how might you seek some validation for your learning on the course?

---

*Activity

**Validating your learning**

Spend 10 minutes on this activity.

One drawback of distance learning is the potential isolation of the student. Here is a list of questions you might ask yourself in order to reflect on your learning and change, and how you might seek some validation for this. Don't spend too long on it, but remember that you can come back to these questions in future learning projects to monitor your own development.

● How have you sought to overcome any isolation and to check out with others how you are doing?

● Have you attempted to interest others when you have been particularly inspired or perplexed by the course? What sort of response have you had?

● Has anyone commented on some aspect of your practice or behaviour which might be attributable to the learning you have gained on the course?

● Have you conducted any 'experiments' with ideas from the course?

---

*Comment*

Monitoring your own change and development can be a lonely business. It's not easy to recognise your own learning. Some people, as they integrate new ideas with their existing knowledge, tend to devalue what they have learnt. It's as though they are saying 'If I know this, it can't be that important!'

It can be encouraging to get feedback from others, even if they require some prompting. The students who act as developmental testers 'do' a draft version of the course for their own learning. At the same time they give feedback on what they have learnt, how helpful they found the activities, what remains unclear. Perhaps because they have been offered the role of developmental tester, and been validated as experimenters whose experience and viewpoint is central to their role, they become confident in offering criticism.

Without some validation from others, it can be more difficult to reflect on personal learning. Maybe it would help if everyone acted as if they were developmental testers whenever they undertook a learning project, whether large or small. ❑

## 8.2  Adjusting to change

To paraphrase Shakespeare, 'some are born into change, some achieve change, and some have change thrust upon them'. Tough suggests that many adult learners come into the middle category. As far as undertaking this course is concerned, you are intending to achieve some change in your life, at least in the sense we have suggested above. Even though you have imposed this course upon yourself in a planned manner, the impact it has had on your life will have been significant, if only because it takes up quite a lot of time. It may have had unforeseen consequences too, so that even if you planned for change in your life you may have been surprised by the outcomes. Perhaps it has caused you to change how you think about some of your own roles and relationships.

We want now to look at responses to change that is not planned and intended. We will ask you to listen to the discussion on Audio Cassette 4 of how people with HIV/Aids and health and social welfare helpers have responded to having had change 'thrust upon them'. This provides an example of the huge impact of some change. However, first reflect on how your experience of change, both as a student on this course and from other areas of your experience, can be used to get an understanding of the impact of change on workers and users in health and welfare.

Activity _____

**Change and adjustment**

Spend 10 minutes on this activity.

Think about your own response to a sudden and unexpected change, for example losing your job, inheriting a significant amount of money, witnessing a road accident or having a serious illness. How did you respond? How

---

*Source*: The Open University (1992) K663 *Roles and Relationships: Perspectives on Practice in Health and Welfare*, Book 3 *Theory and Practice*, Milton Keynes, The Open University, pp. 54–5.

EXAMPLE 3

# Introduction

## THE RESEARCH AWARENESS PROGRAMME

The Research Awareness programme consists of 11 Modules, each dealing with a different aspect of research. It has been developed to assist nurses, midwives and health visitors in understanding research in relation to their own professional practice.

The programme is designed to:

- promote professional self-awareness
- encourage all nurses, midwives and health visitors to develop a questioning approach to their work
- generate a wider understanding of the importance of research as a basis for professional practice
- develop skills in critical analysis and evaluation
- encourage the cross-fertilisation of ideas between practitioners and researchers, based on mutual respect and collaboration.

The programme is thus intended to stimulate your interest in, and enthusiasm for, nursing and midwifery research, although it is not designed as a direct preparation for undertaking research of your own. It will, however, enable you to understand some important issues within the context of your own professional practice.

## The Modules

The Modules are designed to complement each other, but each is also self-standing and can be studied individually. Where a particular Module, or part of a Module, assumes some prior knowledge, this is indicated at the outset. The programme has been developed for self-directed learning, enabling you to study independently and at your own pace. You can organise your study to fit in with your own personal circumstances, and can spend as much time as you find necessary on any part of the programme.

In each Module there are a number of **Activities** which are devised to help you explore the issues raised in the text and to relate them directly to your own work situation; each is followed by a **Commentary** which discusses the important points developed by the Activity. It is often the case that there is no single 'correct' response to an Activity, so many of the Commentaries encourage you to look at your own particular response in the light of the comments that the author makes. The Activities are an important and integral part of the programme; working on them will help you to relate specific ideas to your own areas of experience and reinforce what you are learning. We have given guidance on the amount of time that you are likely to need to complete each Activity; this is based on feedback from practitioners who tested the Module and is not intended to be prescriptive. In order to widen interest in nursing and midwifery research, some of the Activities involve cooperation with colleagues.

At the end of the Module there is a list of suggested **Further reading** and a full list of **References** to publications mentioned. There is also a collection of **offprints**; these are articles and extracts from books that are referred to in the text by their number, and which you are asked to read at specific points as you work through the Module.

You will find a **Progress Box** at the end of each section of the Module. This provides you with a brief summary of the main points that have been covered in that section, and offers a means of consolidating understanding.

## Developmental testing

Each Module has been tested at draft stage by a number of nurses, midwives and health visitors. Some have been following a course in research, such as Unit 5 of the three-year, part-time University of London Diploma in Nursing, and others have participated because of their interest in finding out more about research. While some developmental testers have worked systematically through a sequence of Modules, others have sampled individual ones according to their own particular needs; this reflects the different ways in which the programme materials can be used. Some of the Modules have also been piloted in the context of English National Board Course Nos. 995/870: *An Introduction to the Understanding and Application of Research*. Thus, the material has been critically evaluated by a broad cross-section of nursing and midwifery managers, educators and practitioners.

Furthermore, each Module has been read by Critical Readers chosen for their expertise in the subject area, and the entire programme has been evaluated and approved by an External Appraiser prior to publication.

We hope that you find this open learning programme interesting and challenging and that working through it will prove both stimulating and enjoyable.

## ABOUT THIS MODULE

In contrast to other Modules in this programme, which encourage you to rethink the basis of your practice and to consider a range of clinical and professional matters, this Module focuses on issues and problems of a rather different kind. Here, you will be given the opportunity to develop your skills in thinking through and debating the ethical aspects of nursing and midwifery, and in particular those relating to research. The questions that will be raised are, therefore, ethical rather than clinical. You will be encouraged to think more deeply about ethical aspects of research and to respect differing positions whilst representing your own.

After reflecting on a range of ethical problems, you should be better able to articulate your feelings and ideas and express them clearly to colleagues and researchers. In order to do this, you will need to understand some of the vocabulary and concepts relating to ethics, and some of the particular ethical issues that arise in health care research. There are obviously important ethical considerations that have to be addressed in any research involving patients/clients: for example, it is crucial that patients'/clients' rights are safeguarded.

It is unethical for researchers to undertake, or for health care practitioners to become involved in, a poorly-designed or poorly-executed research study. Whether you are a nurse or midwife who sits on your Local Research Ethics Committee, or a busy practitioner faced with a researcher who wants to use selected information from patient/client records to undertake a research study, you need to be able to ask the appropriate questions to ensure that individuals' rights are adequately protected, and that the proposed research is both necessary and sound.

*Source*: Clark, E. and Hunt, G. (1994) *Ethics in Nursing and Midwifery Research*, Research Awareness Module 6, Distance Learning Centre, South Bank University.

EXAMPLE 4

13

## Section 2

# *Objectives and standards in health care*

In this section you will look at objectives and standards and after completing it you will be able to:

● Define the term 'objective' and distinguish between objectives, aims, tasks and goals.
● Describe how objectives incorporate or imply qualities and standards of service.
● Specify the need for setting objectives and standards in the NHS.
● Explain how and why national and regional decisions affect the formulation and effectiveness of objectives and standards for health care at local and personal levels.
● Formulate personal objectives and relate these to objectives at higher levels in the organisation.

What you do in your daily work is probably a complex mixture of quite different things. Perhaps from making a cup of tea to attending a newly admitted, badly-injured traffic casualty patient. This section is designed to help you to think about the objectives we have in the health care service, and the level or quality of service incorporated into those objectives. You will also be led to consider how various factors affect those objectives and standards. This will help to prepare you for the work you will undertake as you work through the rest of the module.

▶ *Approximate study time:*
*4 hours*
*(including Group Meeting 2 and meeting with your manager)*

*Source*: Wright, S. (1989) Health Pickup, *Setting Objectives and Standards of Care*, Swindon, National Health Service Training Directorate, pp. 1–2.

EXAMPLE 5

---

# ENDNOTE

**Now that you have completed this section, you should be able to:**

- recognise that stress not only affects individuals but can ultimately affect working relationships within a team and the organisation as a whole
- begin to probe some of your own responses to stress
- begin to compare and contrast these responses in relation to different settings and people
- recognise that the issue of stress is important for the qualified nurse.

---

*Source*: Holland, S. (1987) *Managing Care*, Pack 16, *Stress in Nursing*, London, Distance Learning Centre, South Bank Polytechnic, p. 10.

EXAMPLE 6

---

**OBJECTIVES FOR CHAPTER 6**

When you have studied this chapter, you should be able to:

6.1 Discuss the significance of the size and complexity of the NHS workforce for the effectiveness, efficiency and humanity of the health service.

6.2 Describe the division of labour within the NHS workforce in terms of occupational specialisation, gender, ethnicity, income and status.

6.3 Discuss areas of conflict over where boundaries are drawn between the tasks and responsibilities of midwives and obstetricians, and between nurses and doctors.

6.4 Comment on the major conflicts over control of the health workforce.

6.5 Discuss the dilemma facing the nursing profession as it seeks to protect and enhance its working conditions.

6.6 Comment on the strategies available to managers who are required to contain workforce costs.

**QUESTIONS FOR CHAPTER 6**

**Question 1** (*Objective 6.1*)

Describe two consequences of the size and complexity of the NHS workforce for health workers in the 1990s.

**Question 2** (*Objective 6.2*)

What does Table 6.2 tell you about changes in the ethnic and gender composition of GPs in England, and what does it fail to reveal? (Hints: begin with the most recent year and then look back for trends; then look at the totals for males and females and finally look at different places of birth).

**Table 6.2** GPs in England: analysis of percentage by place of birth and sex, 1979–90

| Place of birth | | 1979 | 1984 | 1985 | 1986 | 1987 | 1988 | 1989 | 1990 |
|---|---|---|---|---|---|---|---|---|---|
| all places of birth | **total** | 100.0 | 100.0 | 100.0 | 100.0 | 100.0 | 100.0 | 100.0 | 100.0 |
| | male | 84.7 | 81.6 | 81.0 | 80.1 | 79.1 | 78.2 | 77.2 | 76.2 |
| | female | 15.3 | 18.4 | 19.0 | 19.9 | 20.9 | 21.8 | 22.8 | 23.8 |
| Great Britain | **total** | 73.7 | 73.2 | 73.4 | 73.6 | 73.8 | 73.8 | 73.9 | 73.8 |
| | male | 62.7 | 59.7 | 59.3 | 58.6 | 57.9 | 57.0 | 56.3 | 55.3 |
| | female | 11.0 | 13.6 | 14.2 | 15.0 | 15.9 | 16.8 | 17.6 | 18.4 |
| other UK or Irish Republic | **total** | 5.3 | 3.9 | 3.7 | 3.5 | 3.2 | 3.0 | 2.8 | 2.6 |
| | male | 4.6 | 3.2 | 3.0 | 2.8 | 2.5 | 2.3 | 2.1 | 1.9 |
| | female | 0.7 | 0.7 | 0.7 | 0.7 | 0.7 | 0.7 | 0.7 | 0.7 |
| elsewhere | **total** | 21.0 | 22.8 | 22.9 | 22.9 | 23.0 | 23.2 | 23.3 | 23.6 |
| | male | 17.5 | 18.7 | 18.8 | 18.7 | 18.7 | 18.8 | 18.8 | 19.0 |
| | female | 3.5 | 4.1 | 4.1 | 4.2 | 4.3 | 4.4 | 4.4 | 4.7 |

Source: Department of Health (1991) *Health and Personal Social Services Statistics for England*, HMSO, London, Table 3.26.

---

*Source*: Davey, B. and Popay, J. (eds.) (1993) *Dilemmas in Health Care*, Revised Edition, Buckingham, Open University Press, p. 101.

EXAMPLE 7

© CROWN COPYRIGHT                                            The historical method

## Categories of primary sources

When you have finished listing examples of primary and secondary sources, look and see if the primary sources fall into any natural categories. For example, you may have had in your list the following materials:

—a payslip for the first month you worked as a nurse;
—a rubber Higginson's syringe;
—a china bedpan;
—a photograph of the hospital at which you trained when it was first opened;
—an early nursing textbook, perhaps published before 1921;
—a tape-recording of the reminiscences of a long-lived nurse.

We could rearrange those items under three general headings:

| Documentary | Archaeological | Audio-visual |
|---|---|---|
| payslip | syringe | photograph |
| textbook | bedpan | tape-recording |

Rearrange your list into these three categories.

| Documentary | Archaeological | Audio-visual |
|---|---|---|
|  |  |  |

### Documentary sources

These are the most common sources in the study of modern history. Ever since the invention of printing, documentary evidence has proliferated although, as we shall see later in the module, some important gaps remain. There is a saying, with which you may be familiar, that the "poor left no record"; we shall examine that in a later section but what is meant by it is that most of the written record was produced by the powerful: kings; the churches; the state and governments; employers; and representatives of labour—rather than by the powerless: the paupers; the shop-floor worker; the "ordinary" member of a congregation; and so on. You might like to look at your selection and decide who wrote what; the powerful or the powerless?

### Archaeological evidence

Includes art created by contemporaries: pictures; statuary; sculpture; buildings; industrial machinery and manufactured items; domestic utensils and personal clothing. Which of your items fit this category?

Why have we decided to include art under archaeological evidence? Do you agree with this decision? Which broad category would you put art under? In which category would you put, for example, the painting by Jerry Barrett, *Florence Nightingale at Scutari*, dated around 1856, which is in the National Portrait Gallery, London?

### Audio-visual material

Includes sources created in the media of film; radio; television; or photography. In recent years, the popularity of oral evidence—sometimes referred to as oral history—has opened up the study of history to a wider audience. In addition, some historians, particularly those whose major focus is in local history—the history of a particular community—are looking carefully at folk songs and dialects as important primary sources. You might have included an example of a folk song in your list of primary and secondary sources.

*Source*: Maggs, C. J. (1989) *Exploring History: An Introduction to Nursing's Past*, London, Continuing Nurse Education Programme, p. 19.

# EXAMPLE 8

## Section 7
## Active listening

We have looked in some detail at devaluation and aggression in communication. Let's end this part of the workbook on a more positive note by exploring ways of showing empathy, acceptance and warmth through actively listening to another person. Again we will ask you to approach this 'experientially', through activities which will raise many of the issues we have been exploring throughout this part.

### Optional Activity

The purpose of this section is to help you look at your skills in actively listening to others. One good way to do this is to make a recording of yourself. Before reading any further, make a tape-recording of yourself talking with another person. If possible, work again with your partner with learning difficulties. Make a recording of the person talking about themselves. You could invite your partner to tell a story about their life, like the stories in the course Anthology. The following are some guidelines:

• You will of course need the permission of the person you choose to talk with. You may also need to consult others if, for instance, it is a young person you are going to talk to. If you are working with your partner, you will already have gone through these preliminary discussions.

• There are some technical questions you will need to consider. From past experience we would recommend you to try out your tape-recorder first! You will also need to consider the location of your recording: will there be interruptions?

You might also make this a more two-way process and let your partner ask you about your story while they listen.

(This activity is not as straightforward as it sounds. But you will probably find you learn a great deal from tackling it.)

*Comment*

We shall be asking you to listen to your tape after we have looked at some of the skills of active listening. You might find it useful to refer to your experiences in making the tape as you think about the skills of listening to others. (You will also find the experience of making this tape extremely useful when you come to consider interviews and interviewing techniques in Workbook 2.)

*One friend, one person who is truly understanding, who takes the trouble to listen to us as we consider our problem, can change our whole outlook on the world.*

(Mayo)

We shall now look at the processes of active listening. But these words. 'active listening'. are really inadequate. Listening sounds such an easy process which we don't really need to think about. The Chinese character is far more

challenging and gives a better notion of the processes we shall be exploring. Using the Chinese character as a basis for definition. 'active listening' is: a process in which *I (myself) give my ears, eyes, and heart in undivided attention to you*. When it is thought of like this, listening is not just hearing. it is an intense personal involvement with another person.

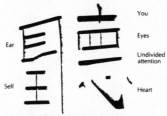

The Chinese character.

Bolton (1979) suggests three groups of listening skills:

• *Attending skills* are ways of being physically involved with the other person in communication. Listening involves our whole bodies not just our ears.

• *Following skills* involve helping the other person talk about whatever they want to talk about, rather than what you want to talk or hear about. The prime task is to stay out of the other's way and not to interrupt or divert their train of thought, so you can discover how the other person views the situation. in their terms rather than yours.

• *Reflecting skills* involve the listener restating the feelings and/or content of what the speaker has communicated and doing so in a way that demonstrates understanding and acceptance.

Let's look at each set of skills in more detail. As we do. don't forget to keep in mind your experiences in making the tape.

### 7.1  Attending skills

#### A posture of involvement

We show we are listening just as much by what we do as what we say. It is easy to see this by thinking of people who do not listen to you. You 'know' they're not listening to you. **S.O.L.E.R.** is a way of remembering about a posture of involvement:

• The S stands for Squarely. A good listener in general tends to face or at least look at the other person. A person who is not listening is sometimes said to 'give the cold shoulder'. There are, of course. no golden rules for listening. It depends so much on the context. such as how close (physical

*Source*: The Open University (1990) K668 *Mental Handicap: Changing Perspectives*, Workbook 1, *Communication: Participating in social relationships*, Milton Keynes, The Open University, p. 46.

EXAMPLE 9

Figure 7: A commonly used memo format

**Structuring a management report**

Before one can begin writing a management document one must go through a planning stage which involves selecting the content and arranging it into a suitable structure. Little advice can be offered on choosing the content, but guidelines are available to help with devising the structure.

Choice of structure will normally be influenced by two main considerations:

• the purpose of the document
• conventions governing the presentation of documents.

These two influences will now be considered in turn.

*Structure and purpose*

As suggested above, the two main purposes of a management document are either to inform or to inform and persuade.

When the intention is to *inform* (i.e. almost invariably) the material should be structured in a simple systematic way that conveys the information clearly and with the least likelihood of confusion for the reader. Haphazard sequences can be very confusing, so it is important to choose a logical sequence. There are several 'natural' sequences that can be adopted, such as:

• chronological sequence of events
• geographical sequence (e.g. deal with area A before considering area B, etc.)
• order of importance (e.g. deal with the most important facts before the less important, or vice versa).

When the intention is to *persuade* it is important to choose a structure which leads the reader naturally towards the conclusions and recommendations which you are advocating. In management writing this is normally achieved by the power of reasoning and logic. Some very skilful writers can use psychological devices to persuade, devices calculated to strike resonances or to stimulate thought-responses which make the reader embrace the conclusions and recommendations as his or her own, but such techniques are beyond the scope of this course. Logic and reason remain the prime devices, and every writer of management documents should structure them in a way that helps the logic and reasoning to emerge very clearly. There are several logical structures which can be readily adopted, such as:

*Source*: The Open University (1991) B782 Resource Book, *Managing Health Services*, Milton Keynes, The Open University, p. 82.

EXAMPLE 10

## Evaluating an open learning package

| | |
|---|---|
| AUDIENCE | For whom is it intended? What prior knowledge, attitudes, skills (e.g. technical, educational, social) are required? Is its target audience sufficiently like ours? |
| OBJECTIVES | Are the learning objectives sufficiently similar to those of our learners? |
| COVERAGE | Is the subject-matter appropriate to our learners and the objectives? Is it accurate and up to date? Broad enough? Balanced? Any serious omissions? |
| TEACHING | Does it teach? Is it geared to learners working with less than usual help? Is it split into manageable chunks? Do learners apply and practice through self-testing activities? Is there adequate feedback? Are they given sufficient guidance on how to use the material? Are media used appropriately? What role for human supporters? |
| STYLE | Is the style of the material suitable for our learners—e.g. tone, vocabulary, sentence length, examples, use of pictorial material? Is it lively and interesting? |
| PHYSICAL FORMAT | Is it attractive in appearance? Legible? Durable? Portable? Suited to how it will be used? |
| REPUTATION | Does the material (and/or the producers) have a "track record"? Who has used it before? How well has it been received by other users? |
| COSTS | How much to hire or buy? What additional costs are there—e.g. video players, support system, staff development, adaptations to package? Is this within our budget and/or that of our learners? |
| AVAILABILITY | How easily/quickly can we obtain sufficient copies? Will it continue to be available? |
| LIKELY BENEFITS | Are learners likely to get what they would expect from using the package? Is the organisation? |
| ALTERNATIVES | How does this material compare with other existing material and with what we might produce ourselves? |

*Source*: Rowntree, D. (1992a) *Exploring Open and Distance Learning*, London, Kogan Page, p. 145.

# Five

# Adapting materials

## Analysing extra needs

Let us assume that you have located some learning materials that seem to be about right for your purposes. But in your evaluation of them you have identified a number of aspects that worry you. These may be aspects of the materials that could have been improved by the producers or aspects that are intrinsic to the nature of learning materials, or mismatches between what they are and what you want. What are these aspects likely to be?

### They are for a slightly different target audience

The materials may more or less cover the ground that you want but they were written for learners in a different context, so the examples given and the descriptions of applying the learning in a work setting 'jar' with your students. Obvious examples include materials on management that often refer to commercial or industrial contexts. Another possibility is that they do not account for differences in law, custom and practice within the UK. England has a very different legal system from Scotland, for example, and in Northern Ireland the health and social welfare system is much more integrated than elsewhere in the UK. This problem will be exacerbated as we increasingly share learning materials among different countries (as, for example, with European Community funded projects).

## They have been written for a different curriculum

Although the materials deal with health-care issues, perhaps they focus on a different knowledge base and different intellectual problems from those of your curriculum. An example would be the OU course U205 *Health and Disease*, which provides a great deal of useful learning for students interested in health care from a number of different occupational perspectives. However, it does not assume and therefore cannot build on any occupational knowledge or experience relevant to health care, and may need to be enhanced so that the connection between the issues in the course and occupational issues can be explicitly made.

## They are pitched at the wrong level

A pack might have some useful material but does not get students thinking in sufficient depth and does not include enough on professional development. Alternatively, another pack might go into too much detail and depth on some key theories for the needs of your course.

## Only some parts are relevant

For example, a pack on stress might start with some useful open-ended diagnostic exercises and teaching inputs on the symptoms and physiology of stress, but then moves on to a rigid sequence of relaxation exercises that you feel are inappropriate for your students. The useful sections of the material may be at the beginning or the end or – presenting most difficulty for the adapter – scattered throughout.

## They are out of date

Some materials may cover your learning objectives very well but have been overtaken by a key piece of new legislation. The problems may be emphasized if the previous Act of Parliament is referred to at regular intervals. This can be a major problem if the new legislation has changed practice significantly. The problem also arises in the area of organizational structures, which can change very frequently within the health service.

## They are not of high enough quality

It sometimes happens that a learning pack has been written by an enthusiastic teacher, but the presentation and production standards are rather amateurish. You might feel unhappy asking your students to use such a pack if they are used to high-quality materials. It is important to be clear about whether it is the learning process or the presentation that is poor; the latter is redeemable, the former may not be.

### They have the wrong ethos

A pack might cover your teaching aims very well but convey other messages that you find unacceptable. For instance, in examples of practice and case studies women might be portrayed in restricted and subordinate roles. Similarly, there might be poor representation of black and ethnic minority people in the illustrations and examples given. Another problem arises with materials that deal with theory alone; they may *be* relevant to practice but might also seem divorced from it because of a lack of examples or any reference to real life situations. Such materials may convey the message to students that practice is not important. Healthcare education is largely concerned with helping students to be better practitioners; it is not the only agenda but it is a primary one. Learning materials can deal with practice in a number of ways, including the provision of appropriate examples and asking students to provide examples. The provision of examples can be in any medium, but the use of video and audiotape is very effective.

### They present only one viewpoint

Students need to think through issues from a number of different viewpoints, and good learning materials help them do this. Some years ago the OU had a substantial battle with the government over the content of their Social Science Foundation Course. The government claimed that it did not deal with the range of viewpoints on economics in a balanced way, and specifically that it did not present the monetarist viewpoint with sufficient clarity. Regardless of the rights of wrongs of that particular debate, which is perhaps remarkable more for its rarity than anything else, you will need to consider what viewpoints should be presented to the students. A uni-professional viewpoint might be right for pre-qualifying students, a multi-professional one for post-qualifying. Alternatively, you may be keen that the patient's voice or the manager's voice is strongly heard. Students may be able to cope with an iconoclastic point of view: for example, professionals who have thought through their professional role thoroughly may be able to 'put the professional view' themselves in a course that presents an anti-professional viewpoint. On the other hand, some students may switch off completely if a course follows a strongly antagonistic line to the sort of practice they pursue. For some to even consider views contrary to their own can appear to be a loss of face.

The idea of balance is often presented as an ideal, but what does it mean? We have recently been involved with the developmental testing of some open learning materials on mental health-care that some students felt offered a one-sided view. We have not yet decided how to deal with this; the materials certainly challenged the students and got them thinking and talking about what views there are and how they differ (and it is important to note that 'lay' students and clients liked them better than the professionals). Have they fulfilled their purpose, or do we also have to incorporate a 'balanced view', and if so, what is it? There are two things to disentangle here. Firstly, there is the issue of whether materials alert learners to a variety of views on a particular issue. Perhaps at an introductory level that is concentrating on breadth of coverage we would expect a summation of major approaches to a subject area. Secondly there is the issue of bias. But at what point does a point of view turn into an unacceptable bias?

Certainly, substantial research is beginning to show that even in highly legalistic, economic and scientific writing, rhetorical devices are used (see, for example, Channell 1990 and Potter and Wetherall 1987). All writing has a particular discourse, that is to say, any events, facts, information or experience can be characterized in a variety of ways. Just as television news shows a particular construction of events and facts, so do learning materials. Often the real question readers are posing is not, 'Is this balanced?' but, 'Does it fit in with my views?'

### *They omit the affective learning domain*

We have often heard it remarked, not unkindly, about learning materials that they are very useful for imparting information but face-to-face work is essential for dealing with the affective domain. But this is based on a misapprehension, as learning materials are well able to work in the affective domain and a number of examples were given in the previous chapter. However, not all materials do sufficient work in this area so it may need enhancement.

### Choosing a strategy to improve materials

So what can be done to make sure that the student experience is exactly how you would want it? Stainton Rogers (1987) categorizes materials enhancement in the following way:

- selection;
- transformation;
- augmentation;
- integration.

In the context of groups not among the designated studentship using the material, she suggests that:

> Being an effective alternative user requires all four kinds of modification. Transformation and selection must be carried out with care to make sure that crucial aspects of context are not lost in the process, but both are very likely to be necessary. Augmentation and integration are, however, essential if materials are to be adapted properly to serve different objectives.
>
> (Stainton Rogers 1987: 44)

The text below addresses these four areas in turn, However, a fifth area of change involves re-ordering and this will also be explored. For the teacher using an open learning programme the final product may be a result of all five methods with some approaches perhaps emphasized more than others depending on the circumstances.

### Selection

Selection of specific materials is an activity that can be carried out with varying degrees of success. Selection can solve only some of the problematic issues we have just raised. For example, it is ostensibly an ideal, neat solution to the problem of relevance. You just select out the relevant parts of the course and discard the rest so that learners will not be distracted. We would, however, mention two constraints on this apparently trouble-free process:

1 It can be costly, if you need to purchase an entire 200-hour course for the 15 pages you think are highly relevant.
2 It can occasionally be difficult to disentangle even relevant pieces of the course. For example, you may find you also have to extract a reader article, an audiotape section, and an offprint, and cope with the fact that three activities cross-reference back to a previous (irrelevant) bit of the course.

Other problematic aspects of materials are *not* easily solved by materials selection. For example, a specific ethos is likely to run through the entire course; a course is going to maintain a simple (or complex) level throughout; poor quality is likely to be evident throughout, and so on. Assuming then that selection of specific materials is only going to partially do the task of getting a satisfactory programme together you need to consider other approaches too.

Nevertheless, it can work well. For example, one modular health studies degree scheme breaks down the eight books of U205 *Health and Disease* into separate modules. Some students take all of them, but each is also available as a 'stand-alone' module. Aspects of cross-referencing, which are not extensive, are dealt with in the supporting tutorials.

## Transformation

Transformation is the process whereby materials with one orientation, view, level, ethos are turned into something more suitable for the needs of the learners you are considering. If selection is like deciding on a particular waistcoat and scarf, transformation is changing the revers on a jacket and loosening the waistband of a skirt. Basically, you have three main choices here (or again a combination of the three). You can rewrite some of the material; you can change the medium of the material, that is to say you can turn text into a diagram or material for presentation on an overhead projector, or audiotape into transcript and so on. Finally you can change the teaching structure, adding to activities, inserting different activities or reducing the number of activities.

Clearly, in terms of expense, rewriting could be a costly option and to rewrite everything is not viable. Again, reverting to the list of problematic issues we cited above, some areas do not lend themselves to a rewrite; where the ethos is inappropriate, for example. However, if it is just the odd case study or a list outlining some legislation that is the problem then rewriting is cost-effective.

Transformation can be a useful way of adjusting materials to suit the needs of your learners in their particular circumstances. Not transformation for its own sake but done as a way of tailoring a learning programme to suit your institution and your learners. Changing the medium of the materials can be a useful path to follow if your institution follows a mixed-mode presentation. For example, if you are planning to hold a number of group sessions with your learners you could:

- transform a number of discursive issues in text into bulleted summary points for an OHP, so that you can draw together the strings of independent study that learners have been tackling;
- transform audiotapes relating to one occupational group by making audiotapes of another occupational group for playing in group sessions;
- transform audiotapes into transcript for work relating to your occupational group for a specialized analysis of communication in the learner's own occupation;
- summarize in textual form diagrams for learners who are not diagram literate;
- rewrite activities so that they pertain more closely to your own occupational group or your own local circumstances;

- transform important pieces of text, simplifying them or overlaying them with more complex ideas depending on your group.

If you are supervising or organizing practice then you could:

- extract important practice points into a worksheet or summary sheet for learners to take with them to practice settings (although we would hope learners would be able to take the whole package with them into practice placements, a summary is always helpful);
- rewrite activities so that they have more bearing on particular practice situations;
- transform text that has been written for academic purposes so that it relates more closely to practice and can usefully be taken into practice situations by the learners.

### Augmentation

The line between transformation and augmentation is quite a fine one. For example, you might decide to add in a couple of case studies or adjust those already available in the open learning materials you are using. Beyond such small-scale adjustments, augmentation is really as long as a piece of string. It very much depends on your preliminary comparison of the materials you are going to use for your curriculum. There are a number of possible avenues:

- to add case study and other substantive materials that converts the overall package into something more closely aligned to your learners' circumstances than the basic learning materials;
- to add a whole extra thread to the materials. For example, you might want to add reflective practice activities specific to your learners' cir-cumstances to the end of each topic of the learning materials thus effectively adding a reflective practice objective to the materials;
- to add study-guide materials to a diverse group of open learning materials. This is particularly likely to be useful if you have selected open learning materials from more than one package.

The sorts of possibilities open for dealing with main texts are also, of course, available for supplementary materials. However, while it may seem that supplementary material can easily be tinkered with (because it is not tangled up with the main text), it is, of course, often referred to extensively in the main text. Deciding to change articles in an offprints book, for example, may mean having to adjust activities in the reading text and possibly on audiotapes too. Similarly, if articles to be read are added, they will need to be integrated with the course materials – by specially written activities, references in a newly produced study guide, or in group sessions.

The basic underlying tasks which need to be considered are:

1 Whether you need to add new 'housekeeping' instructions to the open learning materials you have chosen. The rule of thumb here is the more packages you have dipped into for your curriculum the more likely you are to have to support it with new study guide materials.
2 Whether you want to add in materials that include a new objective (or objectives) or strengthen an objective that is weakly fulfilled in the open learning materials.
3 Whether you want to add in new substantive materials that strengthen the practice support that the materials can offer.

For the learners the most important thing is likely to be their requirement for a study guide that makes sense and draws together the strings of any disparate materials they are offered.

*Study guide materials*
Writing a study guide implies that you are handing over much of the responsibility for directing study over to the learners. Essentially it is an instruction book for how to go about the learning. Therefore you need to put yourself very much in the place of a learner who has got to start from scratch. You need to decide whether your study guide replaces any study guidance offered to learners in the open learning packages they will be dipping into. For example, is your guide going to contain advice on how to go about study? Is it going to repeat or confirm everything learners might have read in the original materials, or just focus on how to put the set of materials together? It is useful to keep in mind as you compose the study guide the example of the instructions commonly found with 'flat-pack' furniture – and of how often they leave you bemused and bewildered because they take too much for granted.
Study guides usually contain:

- a description of the components of the course;
- advice on timing and pacing for tackling the course (i.e. a timetable or calendar): this might also include some advice on how to make the time in a working week for doing a certain amount of study;
- a brief description of issues tackled in the course;
- advice on how to study, take notes, keep records, do referencing, write essays, and so on;
- advice on the order in which to tackle materials.

How comprehensive a study guide should be is highly dependent on the circumstances of the learners. Many distance learning packages (particularly those that are not assessed) need to 'do it all' since the learners may not have recourse to be able to ask anyone if they are in difficulties. However, if, for example, you can rely on there being an introductory session and possibly more than one group session during the presentation of the course, you may also be able to rely on learners getting some of their advice and support from somewhere other than the study guide. So obviously there will be aspects of the study guide that you will be able to truncate or omit; but you need to be sure that all learners can access the alternative provision and not just some of them. Perhaps, then, the central core of the study guide should be advice on the order of the materials and how the learner can best integrate them. Again just as you spend time familiarizing yourself with open learning materials – perusing a good many study guides should give you a feel for ones that are helpful to the student. And if you are writing a basic study guide the best thing to do is to consider the plans of a good study guide as a basis for your own.

### Re-ordering

If materials are split into 'chunks' of learning, which may be in different media, then these 'chunks' can be simply re-ordered. Figure 5.1 shows a straightforward example. The 'books' of the Research Awareness series published by the DLC are used as the learning materials for a research course that consists of two separate modules. However, it was felt that the third book of the series *What Is Science?* offered the students some complex ideas that are better placed in the second of the two modules. It is also interesting to note that the first text of the series is spread over 3 weeks' study time, in contrast to the 'norm' of two weeks in order to give students time to familiarize themselves with study, particularly in open learning mode.

### Integration and Coherence

After the necessary additional materials have been chosen or created, the problem remains of how to present them to the students. Clearly the student will not welcome a published sophisticated learning package plus a sheaf of odd pages marked 'new example for section 7' or 'to replace page 19'. In fact, for some open learning producers upgrading some materials is rather like that and most students end up with a pile of additional papers as well as their study blocks. However, the adaptation of materials can be more sophisticated, and to demonstrate what can be done we will look at two contrasting examples: the workfiles produced by the DLC for Diploma students, and the additional materials produced to update P553 *A Systematic Approach to Nursing Care.*

### Workfiles

The DLC Diploma course, first produced in 1985, consisted of a series of study blocks of text, augmented by audiotapes, which were posted

# Figure 5.1

**ENB 870 An introduction to the understanding and application of research: Structure of the modules over two university semesters**

Module 1

| | | | | | | | WEEKS | | | | | | | |
|---|---|---|---|---|---|---|---|---|---|---|---|---|---|---|
| 1 | 2 | 3 | 4 | 5 | 6 | 7 | 8 | 9 | 10 | 11 | 12 | 13 | 14 | 15 |
| Text 1 | | | | | | | | | | | | | | |
| | | | Text 2 | | | | | | | | | | | |
| | | | | | Text 4 | | | | | | | | | |
| | | | | | | | A 1 | | | | | | | |
| | | | | | | | | | Text 5 | | | | | |
| | | | | | | | | | | | Text 6 | | | |
| | | | | | | | | | | | | | A 2 | |
| 2 Intro Days | | | | | | SD | | | | | | | | SD |

Module 2

| | | | | | | | WEEKS | | | | | | | |
|---|---|---|---|---|---|---|---|---|---|---|---|---|---|---|
| 1 | 2 | 3 | 4 | 5 | 6 | 7 | 8 | 9 | 10 | 11 | 12 | 13 | 14 | 15 |
| Text 3 | | | | | | | | | | | | | | |
| | | Text 7 | | | | | | | | | | | | |
| | | | | Text 8 | | | | | | | | | | |
| | | | | | | Text 9 | | | | | | | | |
| | | | | | | | | A 3 | | | | | | |
| | | | | | | | | | Text 10 | | | | | |
| | | | | | | | | | | | Text 11 | | | |
| | | | | | | | | | | | | | A 4 | |
| SD | | | | SD | | | | | SD | | | | | SD |

| KEY |
|---|
| Text = Distance Learning Programme Materials |
| A = Assignment |
| SD = Study Day |

Copyright © University of Luton

directly to the students. While the students had a personal tutor, they were not expected to be dependent on them but to study independently. Two challenges faced the course team. First, how could they effectively tell the student what they should be doing – for example, when their assignments were due, what the timetable for the study of the study blocks was, when the tutor was available, etc. Second, given that the study blocks were written some time before the students received them, how could they make any changes which might be appropriate to keep them up to date? The answer that was adopted was the creation of a *Workfile*.

The Workfile consisted of a commentary on all aspects of a chunk of learning, which was written and despatched to the students just prior to the scheduled beginning of that learning. It was simply word-processed and photocopied, but input from a graphic designer ensured that it was pleasing to look at and simple to understand. In order to explore what the format can achieve, two examples will be dissected. The first, Workfile DN 404, is related to study of the nursing workforce and was despatched to the students in late November.

It begins by specifying the block of material that the students should be studying over the next 2 weeks. They already have a Study Calendar, so this is a reminder rather than new information. It then introduces both the authors of the Study Block and of the Workfile, so that the students have a sense of who their teachers are and what their background is (a successful instance of personalizing materials for learners). The following section is entitled 'Studying the Block' and gives students some idea of what they face in the next 2 weeks:

> This Block looks at the nursing workforce. It is not concerned with what nurses do, rather with questions about who they are and how many of them there are. There are obvious links with DN 301/401 and the issue of 'manpower' planning is dealt with in DN 407 and DN 309/409 which you will be working on later in the course. Here, though, we are looking at factual evidence for quantitative and qualitative aspects of the nursing workforce, rather than perceptions about nurses and nursing.
>
> (DLC 1988: 1)

As well as introducing the topic in a fairly straightforward way, links are also made with other parts of the curriculum. Such links are sometimes produced in published study materials but they inhibit the degree to which any part of a course can 'stand-alone' as a chunk of learning material or can be changed without affecting all other aspects of the course. However, a Workfile that is rewritten each year bears no such inhibitions. The text on the Study Block continues, and introduces additional activities (here called exercises):

EXERCISE: Can you think of any factors which might have an effect upon local and national labour markets in nursing?

(DLC 1988: 2)

Further text moves on to give some advice on study skills:

Studying the nursing workforce – its character and size – will obviously involve recourse to statistics. This Block naturally, therefore, contains a large number of tables. Please take time to study each of these carefully, identifying trends both expected and unexpected. They do demand a degree of concentration. You may find that during your studies in DN404, therefore, you have to take more frequent study-breaks.

(DLC 1988: 2)

This general text, then moves on to include guidance on many (although not all) of the particular sections of the Study Block:

It might be interesting to investigate for yourself the findings of Davies and Rosser (1986) , cited here, that the idea that women are disadvantaged was met with 'at best puzzlement, at worst with scorn and disbelief.' Does this tally with the views held by you and your colleagues?

(DLC 1988: 3)

This example offers additional 'food for thought' and perhaps reinforces a particularly interesting and challenging point made in the learning materials. Other text on particular sections gives additional information or refers to recent controversy in the press which related to the topic. The final section of the Workfile reviews the topic and offers an additional activity:

For any of you who consider that issues of discrimination are a thing of the past, we have included three recent reports which show otherwise.
EXERCISE: Read the Offprints at the end of the Workfile . . . What do you think of the points and arguments made in them? Have a discussion about these issues with your colleagues and find out whether they share your views.

(DLC 1988: 4)

The Offprints included in the Workfile are from the *Nursing Times, The Guardian* and *Health Services Management,* from dates as recent as 2 months before the study period. Clearly they were published after the Study Block went to the printers and the Workfile offers another chance to bring the material up to date. But in addition, none of them is particularly significant in the long term and probably would not have warranted taking up space in a printed block, so the Workfile also offers the opportunity to include a wider range of more ephemeral examples. At the same time newspaper articles and cuttings that are topical and relevant to aspects of the course can be added, thus relating the course to real lives.

What are the advantages of putting all the 'messages' to students into one Workfile? The main advantages relate to the ease of use to the student who receives one document that serves a multiple purpose, including guidance on assignments. Each Workfile can be filed in sequence and, together with the Study Blocks, comprise the materials. The Workfile cited above was written when the course was newly launched and was trying to predict student problems. But when a course has already been run, feedback from students or tutors about the learning process and remedial work can also be included: something along the lines of 'some students found activity A difficult so we have developed activities B and C to help you think through the issues further'. Commentary from students about the course and their work for the activities can also be shared and this increases the sense of dialogue in the course.

We have cited the example of a Workfile produced as a piece of text. But a more personal note could be introduced by additionally making an audiotape to 'talk' to the learners (or producing a Workfile in audiotape format). Audiotapes are simple and cheap to produce provided no great degree of sophistication is required. And of course in future E-mail and similar electronic mailsystems may be viable alternatives. In summary, the Workfile format can be used to both enhance the learning materials and communicate directly with the student. Enhancement material can:

- replace material;
- add more up-to-date material;
- add examples, perhaps relevant to the students' local experience;
- add activities, perhaps more relevant to the studentship;
- refer to additional resources, possibly local;
- comment on the materials;
- add a different, more personal 'voice'.

*Additional materials*
The course team updating P553 *A Systematic Approach to Nursing Care* took a different view. They did not want to add an ephemeral Workfile, but to supplement the original materials on a permanent basis. They therefore produced a supplementary booklet that followed the structure and pacing of the original but added new sections to each of the original chapters. These sections took into account both the experience of running the course and new research available since the materials were originally produced. The new material followed the style of the original and included new

activities and SAQs. However, completely new sections dealt with issues seen to need increasing emphasis, such as health promotion. Despite the formal production methods, the production of such a booklet to supplement materials is well within the capacity of any HEI.

## Developing new materials

This discussion is very much *not* about the development of materials *ab initio*. This is not, we hasten to add, because we do not know how to do it! We have been at various times, and still are, involved in large- and small-scale production, and can therefore comment with feeling about its difficulties and complexities. However, we know that, despite strong counselling, many teachers are committed to producing original open learning materials, so the following section may be of help to them. Two routes present themselves, first, the production of complete interactive learning materials, second, the production of a 'wrap-around'.

### *Materials production* **ab initio**

Hopefully, ideas about the problems that learning materials have, may serve as a good guide to the production of better materials. In addition, there are a number of excellent texts in this area (for example, Rowntree 1986, 1992a). There are a number of possibilities for attending open learning workshops and resource centres may occasionally run skills workshops. Important issues, perhaps underestimated by the texts, include whether to have a course team and methods of production.

### *Course teams*

The production course team process can be a creative, stimulating and highly productive experience. It can also be extremely fraught! And either way, it is very time consuming. In its favour, we can say that:

- Writing full-time can be a very isolating lonely business; a course team can provide writers with the contact that keeps them going.
- When people are talking to each other it is easy and quick to give and get feedback, to put people straight when they are going off at a tangent and do not know they are doing so. Time can be lost when writers do not get feedback; they can become so attached to their writing that when they finally get criticism they are unable to take it. A course team provides a regular forum for feedback and discussion that at its best can generate a high quality joint product by well-supported authors.

- The process of written commentary and annotation presented at meetings is a way for course-team members to keep a grasp on the whole course, not merely the piece they are writing; and constant commentary can lead to the cross-fertilization of ideas and an integration of a course philosophy.
- It can generate creative ideas and stimulate all concerned.

Some potential problems:

- It is costly. To be successful a course team needs to meet often enough to be a team rather than a group of disparate individuals. This could be a day a week, or a month or whatever. But every time a team of four meets for a day this adds up to four-person-days time (which would, if a team met weekly, equate to sixteen-person-days a month).
- The group dynamics can be difficult. One problem many people who work on course teams find is that routinely putting their ideas on the table to be criticized by other people is hard emotional labour. It is all right while the creativity flows in the early days but can get very wearing after a few months. When the process of your thinking becomes public property and someone suggests that your contribution should be dropped, or turned on its head and reduced from 10,000 words to 3,000 words, it can feel devastating. As a way of working it takes some getting used to, and unless people have that opportunity to get used to the course team process then the whole thing can continue to feel threatening.
- If writers are not prepared to comment on each other's work the integration that a good course requires is not likely to be achieved.
- It is not an easy matter to control maverick writers. It is not actually possible for a course team to 'make' a writer conform. They can offer constructive criticism, annotate texts until they are blue in the face, insist, direct changes, but they cannot make a writer toe the line. The course team process is not by definition an automatic route to good course preparation.

### Production methods

While OU materials have largely established a standard, the production standards espoused by the OU are extremely high. They were first developed in the early 1970s and were based on the prevailing methods of printing and text reproduction at that time. It is questionable, however, whether all students require the standard of production typical of OU products, particularly as the growth of 'desktop' publishing has enabled the range of printing and reproduction outputs to be greatly extended. When the OU started operations, word-processing was in its infancy; now there is a range of relatively cheap word-processing packages that provide excellent text layout for a relatively low price. The last 20 years have seen a revolution in printing and reproduction technology for print, and something very similar for video-production. And like everyone else, the OU is addressing itself to new methods of production. But for many HEIs it has not been until this revolution that there has been any possibility of seriously considering generating open learning materials. These technologies can be used effectively by those wanting to move into production, but a great deal of expertise is still required. A graphic designer may now work directly with the text on screen, but still uses graphic design skills. Technology has made it easier for experts to work directly on the product, but has not diminished the need for expertise. At the very least, any text-based learning package will need input from a subject specialist, an expert in learning materials design (sometimes known as a transformer; see, for example, Fordham 1989) and a graphic designer. The use of any other medium will require similar specialists.

## Wrap-around

Rowntree (1992a) defines a wrap-around as a study guide to non-interactive learning materials. These would include primarily books and videotapes, although materials in other media could be included. The idea of a wrap-around is not dissimilar from that of the Workfile discussed above. The only difference being that the Workfile supported materials that were already interactive, and the wrap-around supports materials with no built-in interactivity. Nevertheless, the list of items potentially to be included in the wrap-around with the discussion of the Workfile above, the comparison is substantial.

Rowntree suggests that a wrap-around may include:

- study guidance;
- learning objectives;
- introductions/overviews;
- summaries;
- glossaries;
- clearer explanations;
- contrasting viewpoints;
- alternative examples;
- illustrations;
- local case studies;
- activities (especially locally relevant ones);
- feedback on such activities;
- instructions for practical work;
- assignments for discussion with tutor, colleagues, etc.

Rowntree points out, helpfully, that the producers of a wrap-around must respect copyright laws, and this applies to anyone reproducing material printed or published elsewhere. The temptation to use a clipping from *Nursing Times*, or whatever, is overwhelming, because it may really help to bring immediacy to materials. But each journal or health care trust or organization will have a specific and enforced policy on copyright. Just to give some idea of the costs involved, a set of learning materials on mental-health issues designed to support 120 student study hours and be worth 15 credits at level 3, which was largely text based but included a video, involved seeking copyright from 43 sources, many overseas. Payments requested (for 500 copies in English language) ranged from nothing to quite substantial sums.

So, again, we counsel against large-scale production, as do many others closely involved in open learning:

> The arguments for choosing one of the other options are thus compelling. Time, money and effort should be saved. The end product is more likely to be good. The energies of teachers and trainers can be deployed in areas where they are more likely to bear fruit, for example in devising flexible support and management systems.
>
> (Lewis and Paine 1985, cited in Rowntree 1992a: 148)

*Six* _____

# Acting the
# teacher's role

_____

We have already outlined some of the teacher's roles in an open learning programme. And we have dealt with some issues surrounding the materials themselves. Now we go on to explore how the adjusted role of teacher works out 'on the ground'.

Because life is somewhat messier than art, the various roles we have discussed in Chapter 3 may be adapted and adopted in very different circumstances and arenas. We have already talked in some detail about the teacher's role in choosing and adapting materials. What we are now doing is moving from 'one-off' or rarely enacted roles to roles that have continuous import for the teacher. Choosing the materials may be a fairly infrequent role, adapting them may be something that needs to be done on a spasmodic basis but mentoring is, for example, something that will need to be done frequently. However, the roles are not isolated, and your own evaluation of a course in your role as a facilitator may lead you, for instance, to re-evaluate the materials that are being used and perhaps to buy different materials in the future. So frequently enacted roles may affect the conduct of rarely enacted roles.

However the roles work out, it is important to remember that the primary focus is the learner and the opportunities that she has to learn. At the same time it is also important to remember that you need to construct your roles so that you continue to get a pay off as teacher. Your roles, as we have previously noted, map on to her roles, so the aim is to get a reciprocal pay off. But the whole picture of student learning may involve some roles for the student to which you do not have easy access (similarly some of your roles do not involve direct contact with the student). To illustrate this it is useful to look at opportunities that learners have for structured and unstructured learning.

## Two dimensions of learning

We want to map two dimensions of learning in a way that highlights your role as a teacher and your relationship with the learners. To do this we use a matrix developed by Nick Farnes that relates to open learning. The two dimensions that he uses are unstructured/structured (learning) and information/experience:

> We have one dimension ranging from relatively unstructured learning to structured learning, recognising that the unstructured learning is likely to be ineffective. The other dimension relates to the content of learning and whether this comes mainly from information or knowledge provided, or from the experiences of the learners.
>
> (Open University 1981: 41)

**Figure 6.1**

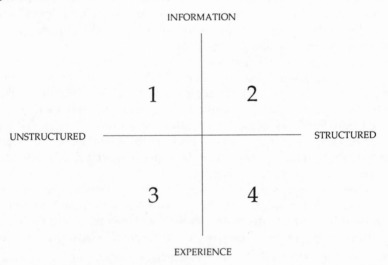

The matrix is as shown in Figure 6.1. In intersecting these two axes, four cells are created. We will call them 1, 2, 3 and 4. The map that results covers most learning situations your students will find themselves in. Not all of them will be learning situations to which you will have direct access, but even those to which you do not have access are worth considering for the following reason: when students engage in open learning much of their learning is managed by the materials themselves. The timetable and support for that learning are perhaps managed by occasional sessions with you, by telephone calls and by the presentation and marking of written work. The automatic support and sharing that comes from working in a regular (say weekly) group session is not necessarily available. Consequently, one of your tasks is to build in as much support as you can using other sources. This means being clear about where there are opportunities for learning to take place even if these are very casual. The learning encapsulated in each cell may take place in a group or an individual arena, it may involve face-to-face contact, telephone contact or written contact. The learning may involve you or other people being used as sounding boards. What is important about the matrix is that it opens up the idea of the variety of learning and helps us think about the teacher's roles as being far more expanded than conventionally. Let us consider, then, the various cells of the matrix.

### Cell 1: Information/unstructured

In Cell 1 we have learning that may involve a casual exchange of information about study that learners are doing, for example, the nature of fractures or the terms of the Children Act. People will go off with new facts at their fingertips. The exchange of information might be straightforward facts or it might be a sort of 'library' exchange where books are cited and sources swapped. It might be people talking to each other aside from the main purpose of a group session or talking together in the refectory. If your institution operates a mixed-mode method of using open learning materials you will be aware of how much your students are on campus in relation to the course you are running. You will probably be aware too if they have other opportunities to meet each other in the institution (for example, if they are doing the same degree course and therefore are together on other courses too). As a teacher you need to be aware that most of your learners are in a network that acts as a repository for information relevant to their course work. However, some students may be isolated and although it is difficult to find this out (particularly if you do not see your students very often), it is part of your role as a facilitator, coach or mentor to encourage them to see each other as a resource (in the same way that you encourage them to see you as a resource). At the same time you want to be confident that the information flowing around this casual exchange is valid and useful. It is usually possible to discern from written work whether some less than useful source of information or distorted facts have entered the student network. For example, in certain subject areas it is sometimes possible to see chunks of crib notes cropping up completely undigested in many people's written work. It is worth taking the time to chase such cases up and to encourage people to use less derivative and more authoritative sources.

## Cell 2: Information/structured

In Cell 2 we have information passing hands by way of structured learning. Technical information is often the main focus here. This may well form a large part of the programme you are presenting, and it is useful to consider the sort of support that you are able to give students. If students have been learning information-heavy or theoretical text by themselves at home, what sort of support will they need?

Although we have emphasized in Chapter 3 that you do not need to re-teach the materials you do need to find out whether and how students have understood technical text. When you ask for feedback in a group session if you ask an open question requesting someone in the group to explain some information or theory this may tell you that one person has understood but not how well everyone else has understood. If students do not contact you by telephone, their written work may be one of your only opportunities to find out how well they have assimilated technical information, unless you can find a way of getting feedback from individual students in group sessions. And we will deal with this later in this chapter.

## Cell 3: Experience/unstructured

In Cell 3 we have unstructured learning based on the experience of the learners. This might be a self-help group that meets to give members support about a difficult situation that they all face or students meeting once a week when they are on practice placements. There is here no guarantee that experience will be reflected upon or developed. Such discussion may merely be a focus of discontent when students meet. Nevertheless, particularly in regard to practice situations, the learning in this cell is a valuable commodity if you can capitalize on it. When students are sharing experience out of your purview then you will need to bear this in mind when you come to work on any sessions that deal with experience (see Cell 4).

## Cell 4: Experience/structured

In Cell 4 we have structured learning based on the experience of the learners. Experience is exchanged and content is structured so that there is a framework in which people can do this. Such a situation can be generated both in group work and individual work. It is really the epitome of the 'involving session' where people are drawn in and their own experience becomes the resource for learning. For individuals learning alone, this approach can be exhilarating and fix the learning very firmly indeed. On the other hand people may feel very put upon and frightened by being asked to learn in a way that encroaches upon their lives. One argument for teacher support in open learning (as opposed to a system where individual learners work on a package at home without any support) is that teachers can be sensitive to the stresses and unexpected avenues that this form of learning can open up. On the other hand there are people who say that the individual learner learning at home can open up to materials without feeling embarrassed and that most learners are well defended against anything in print that will be deeply upsetting – i.e. they will just skip it. (When did you last finish a book that you found too disturbing to read?) When it comes to practice, however, one of your tasks may be to find out what sensitive pieces of learning students have avoided while doing individual study, since it may not be possible to bypass *disturbing learning* for students who are going to practise in arenas where there will be *disturbing situations*. Your support could take place in the classroom, it could be by way of a telephone call, but whichever it is you may well find yourself talking to students about valuing their own experience. If such experience is taken on in a structured way by the materials themselves, reinforcing students in this learning is something that you might want to anticipate.

## The wider implications of the matrix

Figure 6.1 mapped out one way of looking at the dimensions of learning. We have emphasized the importance of considering both the structured aspects of learning (the right-hand side of the matrix and those with which you officially have a role) and the unstructured aspects of learning (the left-hand side of the matrix are those for which you may not have an official brief but that can be really useful resources). Cells 2 and 4 are the ones where the official role of the teacher resides but in any learning situation an awareness that students are also involved in learning relating to Cells 1 and 3 is a valuable resource for you too.

As we have used the matrix so far we have looked at these various arenas as though they were largely independent of each other. Of course, they are not as you will already know from your teaching experience. A student telephones you and wants to know how to interpret some data, relates to you what she and her colleagues thought it meant when they were discussing the course on their practice placements today, tells you the story of how useful it would have been to know it when she was dealing with such and such a patient and is worried about her child-care arrangements. Learning is in some ways quixotic, it is all over the place and it needs to be valued all over the place too. Tough found that although people did all sorts of learning projects they did not really see what they did as learning or value it as such (Tough 1981). Part of your role as a teacher is to help students to do this positive valuation of their learning.

In the rest of this chapter we want to explore five arenas where you make an input as a teacher with your various roles:

- informal networks;
- on the telephone;
- in written comments;
- in the classroom;
- in practice settings.

The first of these *is* an arena of learning but not one where you necessarily have easy access. The rest are arenas in which you conduct your work and where you can provide opportunities for learning.

## Informal networks

In a conventional learning setting students may well spend much time together. In addition to the support they receive from the teacher and the institution they will devise ways of supporting each other: They will discuss the learning, help each other with chasing up resource material and may well even occasionally spend some time together complaining! All these activities support them in their learning situation. But what sort of informal networking exists when a course involves a substantial amount of open learning? 'Not a lot' must be the answer for many students (although students in a mixed-mode institution may see each other reasonably often if they are doing several courses in common). As a teacher you may be able to facilitate some informal links for your learners. Primarily you may be able to facilitate networks that are useful for learners. And networking is about valuing the personal experience of students. It suggests that their experience is valuable as a resource both to them and to other students, without coming on particularly heavily about it.

While you can only do a certain amount towards facilitating networks for students, particularly if they are off-campus most of the time, you can provide the chance for people to get into contact with each other if they want. Below we make some suggestions about how you could do this.

### Talk about networking

Talk about networking with the group when you first meet them. This is really part of breaking down the myths of open learning, an issue we have dealt with throughout the book. People may not feel that sharing facts and interpreting information together is a legitimate activity. They may feel that this is in some way cheating. But the exchange of information among the group can be an important element of open learning and therefore it is useful to foster it as much as possible. Networking is something that is likely to take place in practice placements anyway as people strive to find out pertinent information to be able to do the work that placements demand. And everyone is familiar with that frantic whispering that goes on as people are invited to pass comment on some practice situation and seek the covert support of their peers.

### Encourage mutual support

On the first occasion that the group meet you could suggest students pair off or break down into groups of three and encourage each pair or group to make the time to support each other by telephone, or occasional meetings in terms of materials, the interpretation of data and so on. (This has the added bonus that it may also serve as some kind of personal support.) Remember though, to check your institution's policy on confidentiality. Many institutions involved in open learning only allow students' telephone numbers to be circulated with their permission. Acknowledging the cultural diversity of students is important too, in encouraging networks. Meeting in the pub may be an inappropriate venue for some cultural groups. Meeting at night 'in town' may be unacceptable for some older people or people with young families. Students need to be able to devise their own acceptable arrangements. In addition some people do not wish to be involved in mutual support. The words are 'you may want to' rather than 'you must'! In addition, there are issues of personal safety involved and students should be encouraged to meet publicly to begin with and size each other up if they want to try pairing.

### Develop a journal club

Suggest a journal club where students meet informally to discuss articles that they have agreed to read. This will help foster the exchange of information and it will not be so casual as to exclude students who are not on the grapevine. If the course materials with which you are working involve a course reader or an offprint book this could form the initial basis of such a club. If you are working in a situation where people are meeting rarely, you may want, if you are a course designer or programme organizer, to ensure that there is space for people to meet for such a purpose on days when they are in college. In a mixed-mode course 'teaching days' may be rare and it is tempting to view them as 'cramming days'. As Clark remarks, days when students are in college can end up as days when all contact is teacher led: where teachers focus on summarizing key issues and perhaps alleviating their own anxiety rather than focusing on student learning (Clark 1989).

If you are not in charge of organizing the course then talk to the course organizer about developing a timetable that does enable people some time to develop their networks in this way. You could extend this idea by suggesting that any group of students who work in the same place or are located in the same practice placement could set up a journal club for themselves, since although students may be remote from the institution they may be quite near to each other particularly if they have been put on a practice placement together. Alternatively you could suggest placing students in touch with each other by correspondence, if they agree, to critique articles by post or telephone.

### Working on the telephone

In a conventional learning setting students may bump into you in the corridor, they may save up queries until they see you in the classroom or they may make an appointment to see you. On an open learning course these opportunities may not be readily available to them. Consequently the telephone can potentially be a very important medium of communication. If you work with a large open learning organization such as the OU or a large programme such as the *Nursing Times* Open Learning Programme you may already have a well worked out strategy for the telephone. However, you may find it useful to think about what sort of teacher roles you are using on the telephone and whether and how other roles too can be brought in.

#### *Define your parameters*

When someone is at the other end of the telephone it is not always possible to tell whether you have disturbed them. As one OU tutor recently said to one of us, 'They don't know I got married today', when a student telephoned at the reception! It is important to have parameters for telephoning so that students know that when they do telephone they can expect your full attention. If you say, 'Telephone any time' you may cause anxiety for students because they do not know your routine and may worry they will be disturbing you whenever they telephone. Most teachers who use the telephone as part of their teaching specify when they can be contacted and, having done that, they should expect to keep their part of the bargain: to be 'in role' for the learner. This issue is about more than defining when to telephone, it is about understanding that people are not always in role. This sounds very obvious but it is more difficult for students to gauge your availability at the other end of the telephone than it is for them to perceive that a teacher is having lunch

with her friends in the canteen, and that at that moment it is only acceptable to make arrangements about *when* to talk.

## Identify the person

If you have many students on your register whom you do not see very
often, you need to be able to identify them personally when they telephone. Not doing this is roughly comparable to staring blankly at someone who comes up to you in the corridor who turns out to be one of your
students. We have talked a lot about valuing personal experience. If you
cannot identify someone *personally* you cannot hope to value their experience. If you have the role of a mentor or counsellor this should not be
too difficult because you will probably have made other contacts with
the learner. If not, it can be quite helpful to keep a diary or folder by your
telephone of student profiles. This could be what they talked to you
about when they last telephoned, your comments on their last essay, a
few lines about practice placements they may have been on. After each
telephone call log in what happened; this should guarantee that you are
able to see each student as a person.

## Read between the lines

When someone bumps into you in the corridor it is not always easy to
tell to begin with whether the problem really is as trivial as the student
suggests or whether it is a 'presenting problem' for something more
serious. And the same is true when someone telephones you. Many
doctors report that patients do not raise the issue that has been troubling
them until they have their hand on the door handle to leave the consult-
ing room. It is always worthwhile after dealing with an initial query
asking whether there are other things that the learner wants to raise.
You may even want to suggest a few categories of possible discussion:
assignments, timetabling, work load, practice and so on.

## Develop your own index and cross-referencing system

It is useful to explore the learning materials thoroughly and to make sure
you know exactly where summaries and reiteration of important information are. Be able to refer students directly to pages or tapes that will
reinforce major pieces of information. Similarly be sure that you have a
reading list back up for information that you suspect students are going
to find difficult. Keeping a diary of your experience teaching the course
can be useful here particularly if you teach the course more than once
because you can build up a profile of 'difficult bits' and develop a safety
net for them. Your telephone notes can also serve a more official function

when members of the course team who organize the course come to evaluate what has gone on during the course's presentation.

### Be absolutely clear on the telephone

You may well have quite lot of telephone calls when students get stuck on technical knowledge. If people are in the middle of a study session, they really need to know 'now' how they can get over their difficulty. If any of your students telephone asking for help on technical information, make sure that you have the literature in front of you, and if you do not know the answer off the top of your head then telephone back. Seeing yourself as a resource is not quite the same as seeing yourself as a resource who has instant answers always available. It is often quite difficult to elaborate on technical information on the telephone and you need at least to be sure that you both have a diagram, formula, definition or whatever in front of you for ease of communication. On diagrams, you could agree at the beginning of a telephone discussion to divide them up into quadrants and to number them say, 1 to 4, and that may help to clarify what can be a very difficult discussion without shared access to visual aids. As the course goes on you will begin to get some idea of what is and what is not difficult for the learners and you can begin to develop a series of extra aids that will be useful both in telephone and face-to-face work. One of your functions as a teacher is as a translator of open learning material when students do not understand. We have already talked about ways of making sure you are clear about structures of the course materials. If you are working on a course that does have formulae or extensive diagrams, one useful thing you can do is to prepare in advance explanations of diagrams in words. Students who have visual impairments will want a précis of what diagrams do and not everyone is diagram literate. Translation of the various media into other media can be a very useful ways of providing students with more than one route to understanding.

Overall then, on the telephone you are called upon to coach, facilitate, mentor, counsel and to use yourself as a resource. Like standing in front of a class, telephone work can be a 'pay off' moment when the work that you have done delivering (and possibly writing the course) is transformed into a learner feeding back to you how she is getting on with her learning. Indeed many students telephone for help on assignments that are 'crunch points' in the course and in your discussions with them over these you may well be able to gauge how well they have been doing with their learning so far. But one thing to remember is that many other learners will not telephone you at all unless they are in some difficulties and so your pay off may not always be as positively reinforcing as, say, a lively classroom debate.

## Written comments

Another arena where you work as teacher is in your written comments on essays and projects that the learners have prepared. Again when you do not see people often it is important that you replicate some form of dialogue as much as possible.

### Establish the function of written comments

Some students, particularly those who have not been involved in education since they left school, may find fulsome written comments rather difficult to get used to. If they have always seen 'the red pen' as a criticism of the work that they do then they may think that many comments are tantamount to a dismissal of their piece of work. You need to establish at the beginning (and continue to reinforce) the idea that the comments are intended to be helpful and that they stand in to some extent for the spoken comments that are more easy to disseminate in a classroom situation. One way of doing this is to include a brief summary at the front of the essay about the nature of the on-text comments: 'I think this is a really good essay, my comments are largely by way of interesting points the essay raised for me' or 'My comments mainly pertain to aspects of the essay that are a problem, on the whole you have carried out the task well'. While supporting the student it is important not to back out of firm criticism where that is required. Many teachers deal with this by suggesting a telephone call to amplify and discuss any serious criticism.

### Personalize comments

Many teachers think that personalizing comments is a way of handling distance from the student. If you can imagine that you are talking to one particular student when you make your comments you should be able to personalize them. Include the person's name in your overall comments. Write your critique as 'you' and 'I' so that it reads as though you are personally addressing the student. However, as Harris has remarked over course writing itself one possible reading of personalized feedback is that the teacher has got the right view of the world and that the student is there just to say 'yes' (Harris 1987). There is no easy answer to this except to suggest that you may want to consider some comments (particularly experiential comments) that suggest that you too are vulnerable and not perfect: but it is a difficult balance because you do not want to undermine student confidence in you as someone who has got their head round the course!

## Point forwards as well as backwards

Obviously students need to know how they have done on this particular essay. But it is useful too, to link the comments to the course as a whole and to highlight thoughts or concepts the student has used for possible inclusion in future work: 'Your discussion on dependency was insightful particularly points a, b and c. It should stand you in good stead for the next assignment where you will be able to develop it further'. Assignments are not meant to exist in some kind of suspended animation: they are part of the cumulative learning on the course. It is much easier to stand up and say to a group how the assignment has bearing on the rest of the course than it is to an isolated individual who is doing the course alone. But this sort of signposting needs to be available to individual students as well. In order to do this effectively you need to be able to see what the norms and trends are in student assignment work. And it can underplay the isolation of students if you can say in written comments 'Several people on the course have pursued this interesting line' or 'Several people are having the same difficulty with this concept'. Of course this does imply that you will have time to read briefly through one complete set of assignments to discern any trends before you do individual marking. And then: it is part of your role as researcher to begin to think as to why several people have had difficulty with one particular concept. Does this difficulty lie with the materials or perhaps the dissonance that occurs between some materials and the practice setting: is the student reality and the material at odds? And such questions too feed into evaluation at the end of the course.

## Value personal experience when you have the opportunity

Often students want to get down to the 'real thing' and are not prepared to give experiential learning a chance. This has a two-fold effect. It does not give the materials themselves an opportunity to ease the learner into the learning by moving from that which they know through to more unfamiliar materials and, second, it reinforces the point of view that the resources for learning come from outside the person ('I want to get down to the real stuff, why do they keep asking me about me, why don't they get down to it?'). This is a difficult balance. As they go on, students become familiar with comments about addressing the subject in hand and to 'being relevant' in essays (i.e. talking about course issues) and conceptually therefore it is difficult to see how 'oneself' can be directly germane to course issues. However, applauding experiential contributions in assignment work can help and a written commentary perhaps contributing some of your own experience in a structured way may help too and pointing out places in essays where an experiential account might have garnered more marks. (This might be called a behaviourist approach to humanism!)

From time to time your written comments on student work may be monitored by members of your course team or other colleagues from your college (or you may be involved in mutual monitoring with other teachers working on your course). Such monitoring is intended to protect the quality of teaching. Usually monitoring has a number of aspects: to ensure consistency of grades given to students; to ensure the teacher is handing out appropriate comments in line with the course's aims; to help the teacher with staff development and to provide feedback on how both students and teachers have viewed the assignments. The sorts of written comments we have described above are generally regarded as good practice in this sort of teaching.

## In the classroom

In some ways perhaps, being in the classroom is the most difficult of all the arenas for the teacher to handle in terms of the adjusted role that comes from the inclusion of open learning materials in a programme. It is the place where the conventional teacher role has, as it were, had its culmination and therefore the place where the greatest adjustment might need to take place. In the classroom the inclusion of open learning materials in a learning programme has to be negotiated. But what is changed?

To explore this we are going to use another matrix developed by Nick Farnes that pins down the different components of the group learning experience (Open University 1981). The matrix also accommodates the way the components are fitted together. The basic matrix in Figure 6.2 looks at group work in terms of who provides various components of the learning experience for a group.

The components in the matrix as elaborated by Nick Farnes are as follows:

- *Provide content.* Contents can be facts and information and could be experiences. Essentially it is data, sometimes raw sometimes highly refined.
- *Manage the group process.* This is how the group is organized as a set of people brought together to do something as a collective.
- *Structure content.* Content can be organized into categories and frameworks. Anecdotes can be sorted out and grouped. Apparently disparate facts can be categorized into a larger knowledge framework.
- *Manage learning process.* This consists of the instructions or suggestions to learners to regulate their interaction with the content. People can be asked to compare and contrast, to extrapolate from data, to generalize from facts. This can be done by teachers or by materials.

**Figure 6.2** Group learning experience

|  | GROUP MEMBERS | GROUP LEADER | RESOURCE MATERIAL | STRUCTURED LEARNING MATERIAL |
|---|---|---|---|---|
| PROVIDE CONTENT |  |  |  |  |
| MANAGE GROUP PROCESS |  |  |  |  |
| STRUCTURE CONTENT |  |  |  |  |
| MANAGE LEARNING PROCESS |  |  |  |  |

- *Resource material.* Resource material is, largely speaking, such material as published research, textbooks, recorded interviews on audiotapes, articles, newspaper cuttings and so on. This is all stimulus material and may in itself already be extensively refined and categorized. We think that it is important to differentiate between resource material and structured learning material although some resource materials may have some features that support learners, for example objectives.
- *Structured learning material.* Structured learning material is that which may have content, and structured content at that, but which is distinguished by having learning management in it too. It provides instructions for how the learner is to engage with the material. It is intended to get learners to respond actively.

These different resources have great bearing on the nature of the learning experience. People may want to develop different and new dynamics within their group by using the resources differently. The introduction of open learning materials can bring about a great change.

### Some patterns on the matrix

If you consider a traditional teaching situation and tick the components in the matrix then the pattern would look something like that shown in Fig. 6.3. This denotes a lecture or seminar situation where a group leader

**Figure 6.3** A lecture

| | GROUP MEMBERS | GROUP LEADER | RESOURCE MATERIAL | STRUCTURED LEARNING MATERIAL |
|---|---|---|---|---|
| PROVIDE CONTENT | | ✓ | | |
| MANAGE GROUP PROCESS | | ✓ | | |
| STRUCTURE CONTENT | | ✓ | | |
| MANAGE LEARNING PROCESS | | (✓) | | |

'tells' people some knowledge, manages the learning process perhaps by a question and answer session or asking people to do a written exercise in class and controls this learning process by picking out people to answer questions (although some lectures may contain no learning management and consist primarily of structured content). Thus the content, group and learning are all managed by the leader. Certain sorts of practical sessions might go much the same way.

At the other end of the scale we might imagine a self-help group sharing their experiences and finding ways of making it make sense for them and negotiating the insights and learning that goes on among themselves. In that case the pattern on the matrix might look as shown in Fig. 6.4. Already we can see that the provision of content by the group and by the group leader might lead to very different sorts of learning experiences. For example, in a session about the care of frail older people, a mixed group of nurses, occupational therapists and physiotherapists might well be able to provide all the content that is required, and indeed, a mixed class is very probably able to provide much richer content than a group leader could herself. Such a group may well be able to structure their experience using the bases of their various practices and be able to manage the learning process without intervention of a group leader (although most groups benefit from someone managing the group process). The notion that a group could draw on its own experience and pursue

**Figure 6.4** A self-help group

| | GROUP MEMBERS | GROUP LEADER | RESOURCE MATERIAL | STRUCTURED LEARNING MATERIAL |
|---|---|---|---|---|
| PROVIDE CONTENT | ✓ | | | |
| MANAGE GROUP PROCESS | ✓ | | | |
| STRUCTURE CONTENT | ✓ | | | |
| MANAGE LEARNING PROCESS | ✓ | | | |

a satisfactory learning programme may be less successful in some circumstances. There are situations where personal experience may be an appropriate resource and other occasions where information is a resource. While you might be able to deal with an experiential issue (for example, dependency) by exploring a group's experience you cannot sit around swapping experiences about blood. That the whole group has got blood coursing through their veins is neither here nor there, it is not something anyone is going to want to discuss even in a session in haematology.

Nick Farnes' matrix can provide an opportunity for people to plot out their own use of resources in the way they devise learning programmes. It is also useful as a basis for a retrospective for any individual to consider which learning experiences she has been happiest with and what the balance of use of resources was in that situation.

All the various matrix patterns outlined above have consequences for how both teachers and students feel about their learning. People need to be confident in the type of learning situation in which they find themselves. For learners who have always sat 'at the back of the class' and been lectured to the type of approach outlined in Figure 6.4 could be highly anxiety provoking. On the other hand someone who has firmly taken charge of their own learning and wants a platform where they can try out their own ideas may feel entirely different about a self-help session facilitated by a teacher.

So far we have not emphasized on the matrix where open learning comes in. Below we cite a number of different patterns, relating to the introduction of open learning using the matrix as a way of mapping what is going on.

## Mapping with the matrix

One pattern (Fig. 6.5) might be that a group is using an open learning package and that they come together to discuss their individual work on the area facilitated by the group leader who merely manages the group process. Example: A self-help group working towards an exam meet to discuss model questions and answers. They use the open learning materials to provide themselves with structures to discuss the exam questions. The teacher facilitates the group discussion.

**Figure 6.5** A group using open learning materials

|  | GROUP MEMBERS | GROUP LEADER | RESOURCE MATERIAL | STRUCTURED LEARNING MATERIAL |
|---|---|---|---|---|
| PROVIDE CONTENT | ✓ |  |  |  |
| MANAGE GROUP PROCESS |  | ✓ |  |  |
| STRUCTURE CONTENT | ✓ |  |  |  |
| MANAGE LEARNING PROCESS |  |  |  | ✓ |

Or a group may provide content, structured learning materials manage the learning and the group leader facilitates the group melding the two and perhaps offers complementary resource materials that will help as in Fig. 6.6. Example: A mature group of nurses who trained some time ago and therefore have plenty of experience. They are working through the OU course *A Systematic Approach to Nursing Care* and come together as a group to provide experiential accounts of their encounters with the

**Figure 6.6** Using extra resources

| | GROUP MEMBERS | GROUP LEADER | RESOURCE MATERIAL | STRUCTURED LEARNING MATERIAL |
|---|---|---|---|---|
| PROVIDE CONTENT | ✓ | | | |
| MANAGE GROUP PROCESS | | ✓ | | |
| STRUCTURE CONTENT | | | ✓ | |
| MANAGE LEARNING PROCESS | | | | ✓ |

nursing process. The group leader facilitates and offers some articles on nursing models that she thinks may stimulate the group.

All this suggests that although the emphasis may change when open learning is an integral component of a course, the teacher still needs to orchestrate or stage manage what is going on. Below we offer some considerations for this process, bearing in mind the mapping process as a preliminary to doing group sessions.

*Check the group profile*

To be confident about who is going to manage what in a group session you need to be aware of the profile of the group with whom you are working. How able are they going to be in providing experiential accounts that enhance the learning materials? A group of experienced nurses will be well away in being able to present cases from their nursing experience, student nurses perhaps less so. In situations where discussion of experience is important then if the group's contribution is likely to be sparse then you will need to provide resource materials (perhaps articles from popular journals, case studies garnered from other groups plus instances of your own experience and so on).

Another group profile issue that may be relevant is the hierarchical relationship between students. Where some students are of substantially inferior status to others (particularly if they come from within the same organization), you may find that 'some experience is more equal than other experience' and that people lower down the hierarchy will not willingly put forward their own views. This does require careful handling and you as a teacher will need to try and give everyone 'permission' to talk and be careful to value each contribution.

If the group consists of individuals from a number of different occupations it is important to consider how the experiences of the various members can be melded together. Are they to be considered as 'individual' experiences or 'occupational' ones? And how is your handling of the group's discussions going to line up with what the materials have to say (or not say) about the experiences of different occupations?

### Consider the importance of local information

One area in which the teacher flourishes is in consideration of local information. Open learning materials often tend to be national in orientation. Because of their wide audience they are not able to include specific examples that illustrate local conditions. For example, some quite current nursing learning materials may be very low key about hospital trusts, but if you are dealing with a group of learners for whom trust status is a very important element of how they conduct their jobs, you will need to provide appropriate resource materials, otherwise the efficacy of the open learning materials will be undermined. And if you are discussing something like research then you need to know about local research policies and practice; who key figures on the local research scene are, and so on. But you will also need to be able to fit this into what the materials that you are using say and to be able to work through with students any dissonances.

### Use yourself as a resource

A crucial part of the role in the classroom is the teacher as resource. Because you are familiar with the materials, know the profile of your group and know the local conditions you are in a powerful position to contribute to the discussion. You can use yourself as an exemplar. You are not at risk of wandering off the point with an anecdote because you are presenting your own experience as a model of an answer to say an activity, and at the same time modelling how to think about activities in a fruitful way. No, you are not there to re-teach but you can put your own resource in to model how to answer questions.

### Do not rubbish the materials

Open learning materials are a major presence in the learning arena. And it is very easy to give mixed messages about their uses and functions particularly in the classroom. If you have decided to use a set of open learning materials do not knock its credibility with your students. To avoid this, one useful way of looking at the materials is to see them as a tutorial in print (or another medium) (Rowntree 1992a). If you knock them, it is as if you are coming into a class and undermining everything another teacher has been saying to them. That does not mean to say that you cannot challenge and expand the materials but you need to set this in a climate of open debate. Always think of your open learning materials as another teacher's views. (This approach goes right back to the curriculum development stage.) If you would not have that sort of teacher in your classroom, do not choose that material as part of your learning strategy for your students. This also comes back to the idea of using several pieces of learning material. If there is a disparity in the materials you have chosen then you need to acknowledge this and use it to help students to learn. Imagine again this is like having several experts who are debating in your class. You are the chair and it is your role to help them discuss their differences amicably so that the students are able to see that differences are a very positive aspect of learning. The sense of uncertainty that comes from disparate materials can be very disturbing for students who have not been involved in learning for a while (or for students fresh from school). Certainties are very appealing and do not tax the brain nearly as much as uncertainties and it is a major part of your task in your facilitation of open learning to ensure that students have a safe environment in which to cope with uncertainty. This dissonance is something that you should be able to use positively. You need to let your students be aware that you know there is a dissonance and use it in discussion.

### Do not repeat materials that people have already read in class

You need to be aware of the possibility of getting involved in serious repetition and duplication in your own facilitating. If you have given students a chunk of material to read as preparation it is not going to hold their interest to spend half of the session summarizing it. Find ways of developing what they have done and presenting the basic material covered in another way that requires students to extrapolate on what they have done in their private study. For example:

- Develop a case study for them to analyse in terms of what they have learned in their private study; or get groups of students to develop their own case studies from their practice experience and use that.
- Draw out underlying themes with them. Ask them to apply themes and philosophies they have dealt with elsewhere in the course and to use them to analyse the material. You can use the themes and philosophies of the material itself to do this or you can draw out themes

and philosophies developed in the curriculum as the thread linking a number of disparate pieces of open learning to your curriculum.

- Develop activities and exercises that complement ones that people have done in private study: often the views of a number of group members show up the themes and ideas in an open learning package in spotlight. You may be able to collect such trends at group sessions but if you keep a diary you could well pick this up from telephone calls too.
- Build activities on the 'answers' from activities that students have done in private study. This is an excellent way of ensuring that students do not sail through their private study without any engagement with the activities and it becomes a pragmatic reason for them to do the activities when they are studying alone: it also avoids duplicating doing the activities again.
- Where you can, avoid mixed messages to your students. There is some connection here with the idea of underlying norms and judgements as we discussed in Chapter 3. It is no good on the one hand ostensibly valuing people's experience and then railroading them into a series of right answers that contravene this experience. It is no good suggesting that private study and 'homework' are a really good idea and then completely ignoring what people have done in their private-study sessions. It is no good encouraging people to go out and do project work when you then do not acknowledge that they have done so and do not give them any feedback. Perhaps the temptation to do these things with open learning is more than if you were using solely your own material. When you have 'ownership' of material and ideas you may have a clearer idea of how to argue your case. Not all the open learning materials you collect and use may be materials to which you are deeply committed. But those materials are doing the learning management and it is your job to support them and the students who are using them. The group session provides an ideal opportunity to 'tie the ends together' to get feedback from students about the course.

### Increase the 'voices' who talk on the course

Of course, experience is wider than personal anecdotes about events in the personal lives of your students. In nursing, for example, it presents the potential for a range of cases in which people have been involved, for people to share (but if you utilize this, remember issues of confidentiality). In open learning materials many authors write as though what they have to say is part of a dialogue (Rowntree 1992a). The use of developmental testing comments, personal comments and so on is intended to try and broaden the materials out into something like a conversation. The activity based nature of much learning material is an attempt to foster the notion of a dialogue. As a teacher one of your tasks is to act as a person who can broaden the basic dialogue of the materials into a conversation. What gives conversation much of its dynamism is that people do make personal contributions. You have to 'give' in a conversation. It is a co-operative effort. Your role is partly to develop the most apposite form of conversation to facilitate the learning. Structured learning gives you the basic framework to do this. How you use the experience of students is important for enriching the learning even more. The group session perhaps gives you the best chance of broadening the dialogue to include the learners themselves, you and your own experience and case study materials (or guest speakers) to add yet more to the dialogue.

## Plan group sessions

In this section one of the authors outlines the plan for one of her own teaching sessions.

### Teaching session

Course:      Health and Disease

Time:        3 hours

Context:     The students received their workbooks by post and have the option of attending this seminar several weeks into the course.

Outline plan:
Introduction

* Overview of the course;
* review of study skills.

This supports the messages of the material they have received by looking at the course structure. However, the overview of the course is a relatively small set of additional papers and might have been overlooked – in this session I emphasize that the course structure will be the basis for the assessment strategy.

Although they will either be familiar with the discipline of open learning or will have received written instructions, I emphasize here how it will work in connection with these materials. I go over a page of text showing how they can pull out all the detail by hunting for cues, e.g. first, second . . . , and retain it by using highlighters and marginal notes.

*Major course theme: health*
In this exercise I ask the students to write a list of organizations/institutions related to health (most students list hospitals, doctors, etc. but some go on to list sewers, factories, etc.). I gather in all the lists and redistribute

them. Together we construct a list on the board and draw connections between things.

This is useful because first, it helps the students see health as more than just disease with many organizations involved. Second, it helps students to participate as they are sharing other people's work.

*Personal relationship with the course*
The students pair off and each interviews the other about their experiences, stereotypes, prejudices of health. Again this encourages participation and interaction with peers and also helps people to see their prejudices as such. Usually a number of students have had considerable experience with the health services that they are happy to share. I share my own family history of illness so they can see my prejudices, but I also give them 'permission' not to divulge things that they would rather keep secret.

*'Role play'*
They should have studied a number of chapters on the construction of theories of health in previous centuries. The text covers, for example, the contributions of Pasteur, Koch, etc. to 'modern medicine' as well as discussing previous theories such as humours.

I ask each student to take the part of a person mentioned in the text and split them into three groups:

1 Group 1 are 'pre-science' practitioners of medicine.
2 Group 2 are the contributors to scientific medicine.
3 Group 3 is the queen and her courtiers of Erewhon who have asked the two groups to present their cases for a monopoly of health care in the land. Each group presents its case in turn and the queen decides the winners. Usually she opts for a mixture of both, but there is certainly never a clear cut case for scientific medicine and this is useful for the students to see. It also gives them a chance to work in groups, and develops skills in using the index to search the materials for the information which they need.

*Note*: This teaching session needs to be adapted if the course timetable is different. For example, where the materials are handed out at the first session then this last activity is not helpful. However, this teaching session is easily split into two sessions each of 2 hours, with the additional time taken up with the distribution and checking of materials.

## Practice placements

Practice placements are a crucial part of learning for many people in the health-care occupations. And it raises the hotly debated issue of the theory practice divide. Many writers have presented different and often opposing views (see for example in the context of nursing, Pearson's discussion of the views of Walker, Wooldridge, Rogers, Street (Pearson 1992)). While it is not the place of this book to argue the merits of this issue it is clearly the case that teachers have to take an organizational position over the relationship between open learning materials and practice. In his discussion of nursing theories, Pearson cites Carr and Kemmis:

> A Practice . . . is not some kind of thoughtless behaviour which exists separately from theory and to which theory can be applied. Furthermore, all practices, like all observations, have theory embedded in them and this is just as true for the practice of theoretical pursuits as it is for those of practical pursuits.
>
> (Carr and Kemmis 1987, cited by Pearson 1992, in Robinson and
> Vaughan 1992: 220)

It seems to us that unless students are able to make some links between their learning and the practice placements in which they find themselves, then inevitably they will be likely to view practice as 'thoughtless behaviour'. The great advantage of open learning materials in this respect is a prosaic one: students can take their materials with them to the practice setting whereas face-to-face learning is merely a 'memory' in practice settings. Paradoxically, open learning materials can get much nearer practice than classroom teaching. You have your unit there and you can consult it during the coffee break!

We suggest that there are four things that you can do in relation to practice placements in an open learning context:

1 Prepare students by directing them to open learning materials that can be used to rehearse practice situations.
2 Develop supplementary materials that assist students to use open-learning materials in a practice context.
3 Encourage students to see open learning materials as a surrogate mentor while they are on practice placements.
4 Negotiate with the practice supervisor what her relationship to the open learning materials will be during the course of the practice placements. If your mentoring role involves being the practice supervisor you will need to consider your own role in relation to the link between materials and practice.

Numbers 2 and 3 are closely related and we shall deal with them together.

## 1 Rehearsals

A group or individuals *away from practice* can engage in debate and rehearsal safely and without risk to either themselves or clients or users (this continues the dramatic imagery: a rehearsal is safe, it is not the real thing; people can try things out and make mistakes as a way of getting ready for the real thing). It is an environment where people can be supported through mistakes and uncertainties. Thus the practice process can be rehearsed in the group context. But it does in some way need to replicate what people will find in a real practice situation. Thus in this situation we see that materials can in some ways provide an opportunity for developing ideas about practice by presenting the learners with scenarios that replicate work situations. Open learning materials are often very good at doing this because as they are being produced the learning is built round examples of real practice. For example, a video or audio may capture some aspects of life on a continuing care ward.

### 2/3 Supplementary open learning materials and surrogate mentorship

It is unlikely that the materials you are using in your course will be tailor-made for specific practice placements. It will be useful therefore if you can direct students to those parts that you consider to be particularly helpful for various aspects of their practice. At its simplest this could be a list of topics in the course, their relevance to practice and where they are to be found in the course materials.

But you may also want to link the course to practice more specifically than this. During practice placements students may well need to fill in audit forms in which they log in various competences that they have addressed. Competences may range from being able to describe what is going on in a certain situation to more high-level competences such as carrying out some action without instruction from anyone else. Here materials can act as a surrogate mentor, if you can direct students to where learning support for certain competences lies. The materials may not themselves outline competences *per se* but you should be able to find many instances of underpinning knowledge that will be useful to students. Thus, with some simple 'bridge' materials, you can encourage students to look upon the materials as a reference guide in the practice situation.

### 4 Practice supervision and open learning materials

For you as a teacher the role of the practice supervisor is very important in the practice placement where open learning materials are the main medium of learning. If what the practice supervisor does with the students is at odds with the materials then students may become very confused. You may be supporting individual learners, in separate settings or groups or pairs of students placed together but whether they are isolated or placed in pairs or groups you need to consider *how and where the learning is going to be managed.* Is it going to be handled by a practice supervisor or by the materials or both and if so who is doing what?

If you are not yourself frequently present in the practice setting it is important to be sure how the learning is being handled there. If you are working with a practice supervisor then both you and she need to be clear about the role of materials in a practice setting. In some schemes the practice supervisor is expected to be familiar with and committed to the open learning materials being used on a course (for example, *Nursing Times* open learning schemes have this as an overall principle). If the practice supervisor is sympathetic to the materials, it is a good idea for her, if possible, to have her own copy of the materials you are using. She may well then want to meld certain aspects of her practice supervision quite closely with issues which occur in the course.

Open learning materials can take pressure off the practice supervisor. By using structured learning material in practice situation learners have an opportunity to do authentic practice, well supported by learning materials. The practice supervisor can then concentrate on structuring the practice experience. She can focus on the local situation as it exemplifies the curriculum. Take for example the OU course *A Systematic Approach to Nursing Care.* This contains dozens of activities that focus on the nursing process. For a student on placement the activities and text provide a highly structured approach to examining one's own attitudes and experience as a nurse, in relation to the nursing process. Such text provides a way for a nurse on practice placement to analyse and *document* her experience. Because she has tackled her practice experience in a disciplined and structured way she should be able to come out of that placement ready to articulate her experience. Moreover, because examples of experience are offered in the form of case studies not only is the learner encouraged to structure her own experience (in practice) but she is also presented with other experience against which to compare her practice even if she is isolated in her placement. In this case a practice supervisor can help the learner compare the nursing process as portrayed in text with the actual process that is occurring on the ground. The case studies could form a discussion point: how does this situation compare with the cases in the text, why the difference? and what is the significance of the difference?

Another advantage for a practice supervisor using open learning materials is that because she too has access to them she can press the students: when a student says 'The course doesn't agree with what you are suggesting at all' the practice supervisor can say 'Show me. Show me where this material doesn't measure up with the reality you see.' Thus she has an opportunity to draw practice and theory together explicitly.

Of course, all this assumes a practice supervisor who gives some credence to the ideas contained in open learning texts the students are using. In your various mediating roles as the course progresses you should be able to gauge the extent to which practice supervision is synchronized with the curriculum. However, any discrepancies again need to be handled with sympathy. Just as we have suggested that you do not knock the materials, it is important not to knock practice experiences that the students have had. Just as with open learning materials you are acting as 'a chair' so too you act as a chair in mediating between practice and text.

If the supervisor you are working with is not committed to the open learning materials you are using you need to be clear about her aims and objectives for the practice placement. For example, if her method of working involves little or no reference to the issues in the course or the theorizing espoused by the course you will need to fill this gap. And you may wish to consider writing a fuller supplement of the open learning materials regarding practice. But it is also an organizational issue and it is important in the evaluation at the end of the course presentation to consider how well theory, practice and students have been integrated together and to think about encouraging practice supervisors who have had nothing to do with the materials to explore whether they could integrate them into their practice supervision.

As for your own situation (if you are not the acting practice supervisor) you will want at the least for people to be able to report back in the classroom how they got on and you will want to reinforce the learning that went on. If the learning was supported by materials, you can refer to these in a debriefing session, otherwise you really need to find out what sort of learning the practice supervisor has been promoting so that you can debrief students in this situation too.

However, regardless of how supportive learning materials and practice supervisors are, practice settings can induce uncertainties and anxieties. When they return to the classroom you need to give students a chance to produce their own versions of the uncertainties of practice. If they have been using open learning materials in the field, you will need to emphasize umbrella concepts that synthesize a variety of practice situations, although of course with the understanding that there is uncertainty in practice and that we can never 'wrap it all up'. This is all part of the process of learning.

## Text and dialogue

We have talked about face-to-face contact, telephone work and to some extent about written comments on work. Each medium can serve different functions in relation to the dimensions of learning. For example, your use of the telephone with students may be on the cusp between presenting and reinforcing structured learning and acknowledging more discursive and unstructured learning. On the other hand we might expect your written comments to adhere closely to feedback relating to structured learning. Face-to-face contact including mentorship can go in either direction, reinforcing structured learning but also fostering useful aspects of unstructured learning. As we have noted different forms of feedback for students increase the voices involved in learning.

Onto these equations we have also added discussion of the implications of practice in an open learning situation. Here it is interesting to bear in mind two things that we have already talked about. First, the academic tradition has been closely related to text. Evans and Nation say:

> education is essentially about literacy in its widest sense. The fundamental task of educational institutions is to teach students to harness the technology of writing.
>
> (Evans and Nation 1992: 7)

Second, education for practice is possibly disadvantaged by this approach. We are assuming that most readers of this book will have a particular interest in relating whatever open learning schemes they use to practise. Most open learning packages are currently heavily text-based although they often contain video and audio materials (and, of course there is an upsurge of interest in interactive video in the field of open learning). Perhaps we should modify the Evans and Nation quotation for the benefit of the health and social care occupations and say that *education for practice should harness dialogue*. Certainly in these occupations dialogue is a crucial element in practice no matter how technical the practice field. By thinking of open learning as a dialogue we have a chance to open up the practice elements much more. Education for practice requires a variety of stimuli. We have suggested that in your various roles that you can enhance and expand opportunities for dialogue: in the handling of the materials themselves (in transformation and adaptation for example), in your relationship with the students (in a variety of feedback channels) and in your brokerage of the practice setting (in considering how communication is to be managed using the materials and the practice expertise of supervisors). The overall effect of this combination of strategies should be to increase the dialogue in the learning.

## Putting the roles together

At a rough glance it would seem to be that most of what we have talked about in this chapter has been the facilitating, mentoring, resource and coaching roles: all roles that point firmly in the direction of the student. However, it can be seen that fulfilling each of these roles provides you with resources to fulfil some of your other roles that are more about dealing with systems and administration. Many of the contacts with students that we have discussed are ones that need to be assimilated and used in other arenas. That is to say in your monitoring of individual students and their problems and successes you are building up a repository of information that can help you with your overall evaluation of how the course is going. It helps you build up your contribution to quality assurance tasks. It informs your future policy on buying materials (i.e. you begin to build up a list of features that underlie materials that are working really well), and it helps you see the holes that exist for students to fall into between materials, practice and support. If you find that you are having to build up a complete extra strand of teaching to accompany the practice elements in students' work, either the materials or the practice supervision is not good enough or extensive enough.

It is useful to consider, then, how all the roles fit together although this may not be something that you can actually do until a course is well on its way. A student query can be viewed in a number of ways: as an individual problem with the student's own learning techniques; as a comment on the materials; as a comment on how well the materials support someone in a practice situation; as a comment on how well a system is working and so on. If you have time then you might want to just draw a conclusion about the significance of student queries in this way. Brokerage functions and such like point you partly away from the students because you are dealing with systems but they are not roles divorced from teaching. On the contrary each role within the overall adjusted role of teacher in an open learning situation informs the other roles. There is a web of connections if you choose to pick them up. And if you do choose to pick them up then the various roles can each be enriched by the other roles.

## Afterword

The more you build up your role – the more space it may take in your working life. We have suggested a whole variety of ways in this book that enrich the teaching role in an open learning situation. However, we would close by returning to that most vexed of subjects, money. At its crudest it is unfair and unproductive to expect a teacher to maintain the full panoply of the conventional teacher role and develop extensive open learning materials at the same time. More subtly, teachers may be so anxious that students do not miss out with open learning that they finish up by doing more than a full teaching job. For example, in this Chapter we have suggested that if you read through a whole batch of essays you will have the opportunity to say things like 'several students have pursued this approach', etc. If you multiply this suggestion by the dozens of others we have cited and do each as a major component of your role you will be working 24 hours of every day. In response to this dreadful prospect we would say that you need to experiment and find a range of subtle and small-scale ways of enhancing student experiences. Bear in mind that beyond a certain point you begin to undermine the materials themselves and to go back to notions of conventional face-to-face teaching and support. So if you do feel that you are overwhelmed by your new role we suggest that you go back to Chapter 3 and check your tacit assumptions about what the job involves and to earlier chapters to examine what your own institution is doing in regard to open learning.

# Bibliography

Abraham, F. (1992) *Some Suggestions for Reflecting on Practice,* unpublished discussion paper. Cited in The Open University (1992) K663 *Roles and Relationships: Perspectives on Practice in Health and Welfare,* Workbook 1, *Setting the Scene.* Milton Keynes: The Open University.

Bailey, D. (1987) Open learning and guidance. *British Journal of Guidance and Counselling,* 15(3), September: 237–56.

Bailey, D. (1992) Facilitator not teacher: a role change for tutors in open learning nursing education. *Journal of Advanced Nursing,* 17: 983–91.

Bell, R. and Tight, M. (1993) *Open Universities: A British Tradition?* Buckingham: The Society for Research into Higher Education/Open University Press.

Benner, P. (1984) *From Novice to Expert: Excellence and Power in Clinical Nursing Practice.* Menlo Park, California: Addison-Wesley.

Billings, D. M. (1987) Factors related to progress towards completion of correspondence courses in a baccalaureate nursing programme. *Journal of Advanced Nursing,* 12: 743–50.

Boot, R. and Hodgson, V. (1988) Open learning: philosophy or expediency? *Programmed Learning and Educational Technology,* 25(3): 197–204.

Bosworth, D. P. (1991) *Open Learning.* London: Cassell.

Carr, W. and Kemmis, S. (1987) *Becoming Critical.* Victoria: Deakin University Press. Cited in K. Robinson and B. Vaughan (eds) *Knowledge for Nursing Practice.* Oxford: Butterworth-Heinemann.

Channell, J. (1990) Precise and vague quantities in writing on economics, in W. Nash (ed.) *The Writing Scholar: Studies in Academic Discourse.* London: Sage.

Clark, E. (1989) Hybrid courses in continuing professional development, in K. Robinson (ed.) *Open and Distance Learning for Nurses.* Harlow: Longman.

Clark, E. and Robinson, K. (1992) *Good Practice in Open Learning within Nursing, Midwifery and Health Visiting,* Open Learning Project Monograph No. 3. Sheffield: English National Board for Nursing, Midwifery and Health Visiting.

Clarke, A., Costello, M. and Wright, T. (1986) *The Roles and Risks of Tutors in Open Learning Systems.* Cambridge: Industrial Training Research Unit.

Coopers & Lybrand (1989) *A Report into the Relative Costs of Open Learning.* Sheffield: Open University/Employment Department. Cited in D. Rowntree (1992a) *Exploring Open and Distance Learning.* London: Kogan Page.

Council for National Academic Awards (1987) *The Feasibility of Adapting Open University Material for Use in Polytechnics and Similar Institutions,* summary of the report of a CNAA Development Fund project at Huddersfield Polytechnic, Development Services Briefing No. 1, June. London: CNAA.

Davey, B. and Popay, J. (eds) (1993) *Dilemmas in Health Care,* rev. edn. Buckingham: Open University Press.

Dhanarajan, G. and Timmers, S. (1992) Transfer and adaptation of self-instructional materials. *Open Learning,* 7(1): 3–11.

Distance Learning Centre (1987a) *Managing Care,* Pack 16, *Stress in Nursing.* London: Distance Learning Centre, South Bank Polytechnic.

Distance Learning Centre (1987b) Research Awareness Module 5, *Identifying and Defining Questions for Research.* London: Distance Learning Centre, South Bank Polytechnic.

Distance Learning Centre (1988) Workfile Block DN 404. London: Distance Learning Centre, South Bank Polytechnic.

Evans, T. and Nation, D. (1992) Theorising open and distance education. *Open Learning,* 7(2), June: 3–13.

Evans, T. and Nation, D. (eds) (1993) *Reforming Open and Distance Education: Critical Reflections from Practice.* London: Routledge and Kegan Paul.

Faith, K. (ed.) (1988) *Toward New Horizons for Women in Distance Education, International Perspectives.* London: Routledge.

Farnes, N. (1981) *See* Open University 1981.

Fordham, J. (1989) The role of the open learning editor, in K. Robinson (ed.) *Open and Distance Learning for Nurses.* Harlow: Longman.

Freeman, R. (1991) Quality assurance in learning materials. *Open Learning,* 6(3): 24–31.

Gagné, R. M. (1965) *The Conditions of Learning.* New York: Rinehart and Winston.

Gilliard, G. (1993) Deconstructing contiguity, in D. Evans and T. Nation (eds) *Reforming Open and Distance Education: Critical Reflections from Practice.* London: Routledge and Kegan Paul.

Goffman, E. (1959) *Presentation of Self in Everyday Life.* New York: Doubleday Anchor.

Goffman, E. (1972) *Frame Analysis.* Harmondsworth: Penguin.

Green, W. (1989) Helping bank nurses, in K. Robinson (ed.) *Open and Distance Learning for Nurses.* Harlow: Longman.

Grugeon, D. (1987) Education counselling and open learning, in M. Thorpe and D. Grugeon (eds) *Open Learning for Adults.* Harlow: Longman.

Hammersley, M. (1986) *Case Studies in Classroom Research.* Milton Keynes: Open University Press.

Harris, D. (1987) *Openness and Closure in Distance Education.* London: Falmer Press.

Hart, G. (1990) Peer learning and support via audio-teleconferencing in continuing education for nurses. *Distance Education,* 11(2): 308–19.

Hodgson, B. (1993) *Key Terms and Issues in Open and Distance Learning.* London: Kogan Page.

Johns, C. C. (1994) Guided reflection, in A. Palmer, S. Burns and C. Bulman (eds) *Reflective Practice in Nursing: The Growth of the Professional Practitioner.* Oxford: Blackwell.

Johnston, M. (1989) Helping enrolled nurses, in K. Robinson (ed.) *Open and Distance Learning for Nurses.* Harlow, Longman.

Lemark, B. (1986) *A Distance Education Programme for Training Nursing Teachers, Department of Educational and Psychological Research,* Malmo School of Education – University of Lund No. 547, Reprints and Miniprints, November.

Le Var, R. (1992) Current initiatives in open learning, *Nursing Standard,* 6(52), 16 September: 34–5.

Lewis, R. and Paine, N. (1985) *How to Find and Adapt Materials and Select Media.* London: Council for Education Technology. Cited in D. Rowntree (1992a) *Exploring Open and Distance Learning.* London: Kogan Page.

Lewis, R. and Spencer, D. (1986) *What Is Open Learning?* London: Council for Educational Technology.

Lister, P. (1991) Approaching models of nursing from a post-modernist perspective. *Journal of Advanced Nursing,* 16: 206–12. Cited in Bailey, D. (1992) Facilitator not teacher: a role change for tutors in open learning nursing education, *Journal of Advanced Nursing,* 17: 983–91.

Lockwood, F. G. (1990) 'Activities in Distance Learning Texts', unpublished PhD thesis. Milton Keynes, The Open University.

Maggs, C. J. (1989) *Exploring History: An Introduction to Nursing's Past.* London: Continuing Nurse Education Programme.

Manpower Services Commission (1988) *Ensuring Quality in Open Learning: A Handbook for Action.* Sheffield: Manpower Services Commission.

Murgatroyd, S. (1980) What actually happens in tutorials?, *Teaching at a Distance,* 18, winter: 44–53.

Open University, the (1981) *Development and Use of Parent Education Materials,* Second year report from The Open University submitted to the Bernard Van Leer Foundation, September. Milton Keynes: Community Education/The Open University.

Open University, the (1987) Project Management (internal paper), cited in B. Robinson (1992). Applying quality standards in distance and open learning. *EADTU News,* issue 11, September: 11–17.

Open University, the (1989) P553 *A Systematic Approach to Nursing Care,* 2nd edn. Milton Keynes: The Open University.

Open University, the (1990) K668 *Mental Handicap: Changing Perspectives,* Workbook 1, *Communication: Participating in social relationships.* Milton Keynes: The Open University.

Open University, the (1991) B782 Resource Book *Managing Health Services.* Milton Keynes: The Open University.

Open University, the (1994) *Health and Disease.* Milton Keynes: The Open University.

Open University, the (1992) K663 *Roles and Relationships: Perspectives on Practice in Health and Welfare,* Book 3, *Theory and Practice.* Milton Keynes: The Open University.

Open University, the (1992) K663 *Roles and Relationships: Perspectives on Practice in Health and Welfare*, Workbook 1, *Setting the Scene*. Milton Keynes: The Open University.

Open University, the/Department of Employment (1990) *How to Profit from Open Learning – Company Evidence*. Milton Keynes: The Open University/Department of Employment.

Pearson, A. (1992) Knowing nursing: emerging paradigms in nursing, in K. Robinson and B. Vaughan (eds) *Knowledge for Nursing Practice*. Oxford: Butterworth-Heinemann.

Perry, W. (1976) *Open University*. Milton Keynes: Open University Press.

Potter, J. and Wetherall, M. (1987) *Discourse and Social Psychology*. London: Sage.

Project Management, Open University, UK 1987, cited in Robinson (1992).

Pugh, D. S. and Hickson, D. J. (eds) (1989) *Writers on Organizations*, new edn. London: Penguin.

Pym, F. R. (1992) Women and distance education: a nursing perspective. *Journal of Advanced Nursing*, 17: 383–9.

Race, P. (1989) *The Open Learning Handbook*. London: Kogan Page.

Robinson, B. (1992) Applying quality standards in distance and open learning. *EADTU News*, issue 11, September: 11–17.

Robinson, K. (ed.) (1989) *Open and Distance Learning for Nurses*. Harlow, Essex: Longman.

Robinson, K. and Clark, E. (1992) *Costing Open Learning: Factors for Consideration*, Open Learning Project Monograph No. 4. Sheffield: English National Board for Nursing, Midwifery and Health Visiting.

Robinson, K. Robinson, H. and Hilton, A. (1992) Research Awareness Module 3, *What is Research?*, London, Distance Learning Centre, South Bank Polytechnic.

Robinson, K. and Vaughan, B. (eds) (1992) *Knowledge for Nursing Practice*. Oxford: Butterworth-Heinemann.

Rowntree, D. (1986) *Teaching Through Self Instruction: A Practical Handbook for Course Developers*. London: Kogan Page.

Rowntree, D. (1992a) *Exploring Open and Distance Learning*. London: Kogan Page.

Rowntree, D. (1992b) *Teach Yourself with Open Learning*. London: Sphere Books.

Royal College of Nursing (1994a) RCN Nursing Update Learning Unit 006 *Wound Care: A Problem Solving Approach. Nursing Standard*, 8(19), 2 February: supplement.

Royal College of Nursing (1994b) RCN Nursing Update Learning Unit 008 *A Healthy Skin. Nursing Standard*, 8(17), 19 January: supplement.

Rumble, G. (1988) The economics of mass distance education. *Prospects*, XVIII(1): 91–102.

Rumble, G. (1992) The competitive vulnerability of distance teaching universities, *Open Learning*, 7(2), June: 31–45.

Rumble, G. and Harry, K. (eds) (1982) *The Distance Teaching Universities*. London: Croom Helm.

Schön, D. (1991) *The Reflective Practitioner: How Professionals Think in Action*. Aldershot: Avebury.

Stainton Rogers, W. (1987) Adapting materials to alternative use, in M. Thorpe and D. Grugeon (eds) *Open Learning for Adults*. Harlow: Longman.

Thorpe, M. (1988) *Evaluating Open and Distance Learning*. Harlow: Longman.

Tough, A. (1981) *Learning without a Teacher. A Study of Tasks and Assistance During Adult Self Teaching Project*, Educational Research Series, No. 3. Ontario Institute for Studies in Education.

Tough, A. (1982) *Intentional Changes. A Fresh Approach to Helping People Change.* Chicago: Follett Publishing Company.

University of South Australia. (1993) UED 601 *Issues and Methods in Research.* Underdale, South Australia: Distance Education Centre, University of South Australia.

Wakeling, C. (1989) Highland Health Board: a co-ordinated scheme, in K. Robinson (ed.) *Open and Distance Learning for Nurses.* Harlow: Longman.

Webster, C. (ed.) (1993) *Caring for Health: History and Diversity*, rev. edn. Buckingham: Open University Press, pp. 150–1.

Wright, S. (1989) Health Pickup, *Setting Objectives and Standards of Care.* Swindon, National Health Service Training Directorate.

Wright, T. (1991) Book review: the management of quality, Open College, *Open Learning*, 6(3), November: 64–6.

# Index

access, 24, 44
accreditation, 42
  of prior experiential learning (APEL),
    32
  product-based, 42
  value-based, 42
activities, 64, 73, 82–3
  and assessment, 83
  cost benefit analysis, 64
  exercises, 82
  group activities, 83
  in-text questions (ITQs), 82
  orienting questions, 73
  self-assessment questions (SAQs), 73,
    82, 113
adapting materials, 4, 29, 70, 144
  affective domain, 103
  audience, 100
  balance, 102
  cost-effectiveness, 16
  curriculum, 101
  date, 101
  ethos, 102
  level, 101
  quality, 101
  relevance, 101
  viewpoint, 102
  *see also* materials
additional materials, 112–13
administrative tasks, 40
administrators, 29
assignments, 35, 128

audiotapes, 28
  as aids to diagrams, 82
  as responses to practice, 82
  *see also* materials
augmentation of open learning
  materials, 106
  adding extra case studies, 106
  adding extra themes, 106
  *see also* study guides

Barnet FE college, 14

*Child Abuse and Neglect*, 84
choosing materials, 4
  *see also* materials
classroom work on open learning,
  129–39
  activities, 137
  case studies, 136
  credibility of materials, 135–6
  experiential approach, 55
  face-to-face contact, 37, 59
  group process, 129
  group profile, 134
  group sessions, 138–9
  local information, 56, 135
  repetition, 37
  *see also* teacher
clinical work, 28
CNAA, 10, 11
competences, 141
computer networking, 5